EVERY CHILD'S STORY BOOK

Every Child's Story Book

A HORN OF PLENTY OF GOOD READING

FOR BOYS AND GIRLS

SELECTED BY

Margaret Martignoni

formerly Superintendent of Work with Children
Brooklyn Public Library, New York

ILLUSTRATED BY GIOIA FIAMMENGHI

FRANKLIN WATTS, INC.

575 LEXINGTON AVENUE
NEW YORK 22, N. Y.

ACKNOWLEDGMENTS

The selections reprinted in this anthology are used by permission and special arrangement with the proprietors of their respective copyrights, who are listed below. The compiler's and publisher's thanks to all who helped make this collection possible.

Abingdon Press
for "The Climb," from *Li Lun, Lad of Courage*, by Carolyn Treffinger. Copyright 1947 by Stone and Pierce. Used by permission of Abingdon Press, publishers.

Appleton-Century-Crofts, Inc.
for "How the Turtle Saved his own Life," "The Foolish, Timid Rabbit," and "The Quarrel of the Quails," from *Jataka Tales*, by Ellen C. Babbitt. Copyright 1912 by The Century Co. Reprinted by permission of the publishers Appleton-Century-Crofts, Inc.

Coward-McCann, Inc.
for *The Five Chinese Brothers*, by Claire Huchet Bishop. Reprinted by permission of Coward-McCann, Inc., copyright 1938 by Claire Huchet Bishop and Kurt Wiese, illustrated by Kurt Wiese.

Thomas Y. Crowell Company
for *A Pussycat's Christmas*, by Margaret Wise Brown. Copyright 1949 by Margaret Wise Brown.
for "Playing Paper Dolls," from *Betsy-Tacy*, by Maud Hart Lovelace. Copyright 1940 by Maud Hart Lovelace.
for "The Runaway Pony," from *Surprise for a Cowboy*, by Clyde Robert Bulla. Copyright 1950 by Clyde Robert Bulla.

Doubleday & Company, Inc.
for selection from *Ted and Nina Have a Happy Rainy Day*, by Marguerite de Angeli. Copyright 1936 by Marguerite de Angeli. Reprinted by permission of Doubleday & Company, Inc.
for "The Two Stone Giants," from *Tales of a Korean Grandmother*, by Frances Carpenter. Copyright 1947 by Frances Carpenter Huntington. Reprinted by permission of Doubleday & Co., Inc.
for "The Pretzel Man," "The Animal Store," and

"Vegetables," from *Taxis and Toadstools*, by Rachel Field. Copyright 1926 by Doubleday & Company, Inc. Reprinted by permission.
for "If you Meet a Fairy," from *The Fairy Flute*, by Rose Fyleman. Copyright 1923 by George H. Doran. Reprinted by permission of Doubleday & Company, Inc.
for "The Poppy Seed Cakes," from *The Poppy Seed Cakes*, by Margery Clark. Copyright 1924 by Doubleday & Company, Inc. Reprinted by permission of the publisher.
for *Angus and the Ducks*, by Marjorie Flack. Copyright 1930 by Doubleday & Company, Inc. Reprinted by permission of the publisher.

E. P. Dutton & Co., Inc.
for "The Tea Party," copyright, 1932, by Marchette Chute; and "Drinking Fountain," copyright 1946 by Marchette Chute. From the book *Around and About*, by Marchette Chute; published by E. P. Dutton & Co., Inc., 1957. Reprinted with their permission.
for selection from *Meph, the Pet Skunk*, by John and Jean George. Copyright 1952 by E. P. Dutton & Co., Inc. Reprinted with their permission.

Follett Publishing Company
for "Dusting Is Fun," from *All-of-a-kind Family*, by Sydney Taylor. Copyright held by Follett Publishing Company, Chicago.

Harcourt, Brace and Company, Inc.
for "Trees," from *The Little Hill*, copyright 1949 by Harry Behn. Reprinted by permission of Harcourt, Brace and Company, Inc.
for "The Wonderful Knapsack," from *13 Danish Tales*, retold by Mary C. Hatch. Copyright 1947 by Harcourt, Brace and Company, Inc. and reprinted with their permission.
for "It's Fun To Slide on the Banister," from *Two and Two Are Four*, by Carolyn Haywood. Copyright 1940 by Harcourt, Brace and Company, Inc.
for "Betsy Goes to School and Finds a Big Surprise," from *B Is for Betsy*, by Carolyn Haywood.

Magic, by Julia L. Sauer. Copyright 1943 by Julia L. Sauer. Reprinted by permission of The Viking Press, Inc., New York.

for "Margaret," from *In and Out,* by Tom Robinson. Copyright 1943 by Tom Robinson. Reprinted by permission of The Viking Press, Inc.

Henry Z. Walck, Inc.

for selection from *Azor,* by Maude Crowley. Copyright 1948 by Henry Z. Walck, Inc. Reprinted by permission.

for "The Little Lady's Roses," from *The Little Bookroom,* by Eleanor Farjeon. Copyright 1955 by Eleanor Farjeon. Reprinted by permission of Henry Z. Walck, Inc.

Franklin Watts, Inc.

for selections from *Lavender's Blue,* edited by Kathleen Lines, 1954. Reprinted by permission.

for "The Enemy," from *The Favorite Place,* by Irmengarde Eberle. Copyright 1957 by Irmengarde Eberle Koehler. Reprinted by permission.

for "Riddle This, Riddle That," from *This Boy Cody.* Copyright 1950 by Leon Wilson. Reprinted by permission of Franklin Watts, Inc.

for selections from *Riddles, Riddles, Riddles,* edited by Joseph Leeming. Copyright 1953 by Franklin Watts, Inc. Reprinted by permission.

for "Beauty and the Beast," "Puss-in-Boots," "The Boy Who Went to the North Wind," from *The First Book of Fairy Tales,* retold by Elizabeth Abell. Copyright 1958 by Franklin Watts, Inc. Reprinted by permission.

for selections from *Jokes, Jokes, Jokes,* edited by Helen Hoke. Copyright 1954 by Franklin Watts, Inc. Reprinted by permission.

for selections from *The Giant Book of Family Fun and Games,* edited by Jack Tedford. Copyright 1958 by Franklin Watts, Inc. Reprinted by permission.

for *The Horn that Stopped the Band,* by Arthur H. Parsons, Jr. Copyright 1954 by Franklin Watts, Inc. Reprinted by permission.

For Dad

because he loves children
and books

CONTENTS

PART II

PART III

INTRODUCTION

WHO LIKES to have fun? Everyone, of course! But especially boys and girls. Having fun is a very important part of growing up.

Fortunately, there are many different ways of having fun, and a wise boy or girl will take advantage of all of them. Running and racing, playing games, and riding bicycles out-of-doors. Listening to the radio, watching television, and playing phonograph records indoors. And best of all for many of us — reading books. For reading can be lots of fun too.

Books are eager to be your "best friends" for life. They can be enjoyed indoors, outdoors, wherever you happen to be. People read books in trains and buses, on ships at sea, and while flying through the sky in airplanes. They read sprawled on their stomachs under beach umbrellas, while waiting apprehensively in doctors' offices, and — although your mother may not approve — some people even read in the bathtub! Soldiers have been known to carry pocket volumes onto the battlefield and to read while waiting in foxholes or behind barricades. And, of course, thousands of people read comfortably safe and sound in their own beds before going to sleep at night.

A book is always ready and waiting for you. It doesn't get a flat tire, or need an electric outlet or batteries, and it never blows a tube. Given reasonable care it will last a lifetime or longer. Its magic spell always remains the same, with the familiar scenes and characters ready to spring to life again the moment the pages are opened.

This book is really a horn of plenty — a jolly cornucopia chock full of reading delights for boys and girls. Except for the nursery rhymes and folk tales, these selections are the work of modern writers. They represent many kinds of reading, some of which will appeal to you more than others. But all are fun to read.

When one of these stories has been taken from a longer work, the full name of the book is given at the end of the selection. For still more fun, follow up your favorites and read more from the same book.

And now, jump in and enjoy yourself. This horn of plenty has something for each of you.

Margaret E. Martignoni

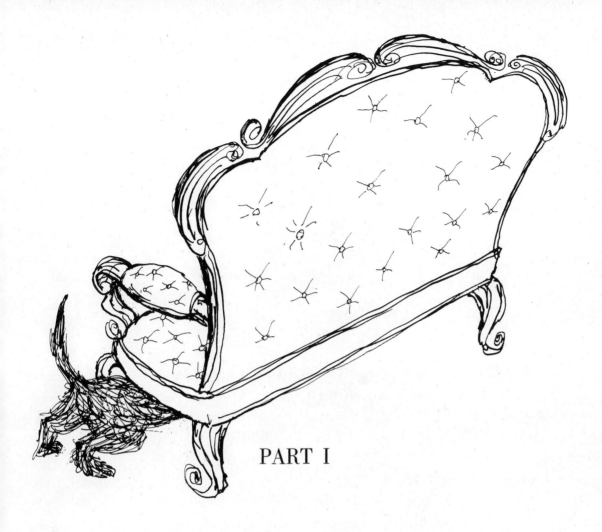

PART I

ANGUS AND THE DUCKS

Marjorie Flack

*Most of us are curious about something at least
once in a while. Angus was curious all the time!*

ONCE THERE WAS a very young little dog whose name was Angus, because his mother and his father came from Scotland.

Although the rest of Angus was quite small, his head was very large and so were his feet.

Angus was curious about many places and many things:

He was curious about WHAT lived under the sofa and in dark corners and WHO was the little dog in the mirror.

He was curious about Things-

1

QUACK·K·K·K·K

Which-Come-Apart and those Things-Which-Don't-Come-Apart; such as SLIPPERS and gentlemen's SUSPENDERS and things like that.

Angus was also curious about Things-Outdoors but he could not find out much about them because of a leash.

The leash was fastened at one end to the collar around his neck and at the other end to SOMEBODY ELSE.

But Angus was most curious of all about a NOISE which came from the OTHER SIDE of the large green hedge at the end of the garden.

The noise usually sounded like this: Quack! Quack! Quackety! Quack!!

But sometimes it sounded like this: Quackety! Quackety! Quackety! Quack!!

One day the door between OUTDOORS and INDOORS was left open by mistake; and out went Angus without the leash or SOMEBODY ELSE.

Down the little path he ran until he came to the large green hedge at the end of the garden.

He tried to go around it but it was much too long. He tried to go over it but it was much too high. So Angus went under the large green hedge and came out on the OTHER SIDE.

There, directly in front of him, were two white DUCKS. They were marching forward, one-foot-up and one-foot-down. Quack! Quack! Quackety! Quack!!!

Angus said: WOO-OO-OOF!!!

Away went the DUCKS all of a flutter. Quackety! Quackety! Quackety! Quackety! Quackety!!!

Angus followed after.

Soon the DUCKS stopped by a stone watering trough under a mulberry tree.

Angus stopped, too. Each DUCK dipped a yellow bill in the clear cool water. Angus watched. Each DUCK took a long drink of the cool clear water. Still Angus watched. Each DUCK took another long drink of cool clear water.

Then Angus said: WOO-OO-OOF!

Away the DUCKS scuttled and Angus lapped the cool clear water.

Birds sang in the mulberry tree.

The Sun made patterns through the leaves over the grass.

The DUCKS talked together: Quack! Quack! Quack! Then: HISS-S-S-S-S-S-S!!! HISS-S-S-S-S-S-S!!!

The first DUCK nipped Angus's tail! HISS-S-S-S-S-S-S!!! HISS-S-S-S-S-S-S!!!

The second DUCK flapped his wings!

Angus scrambled under the large green hedge, scurried up the little path, scampered into the house and crawled under the sofa.

For exactly THREE minutes by the clock, Angus was NOT curious about anything at all.

Conclusion:

There are many pictures about this story in the book *Angus and the Ducks*, by Marjorie Flack, published by Doubleday & Company, Inc. You can read about other adventures of this mischievous little Scottie in *Angus and the Cat* and *Angus Lost*.

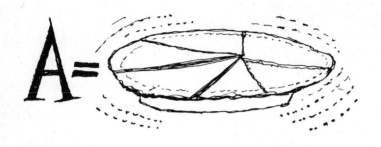

A **was an Apple-Pie**

A was an Apple-Pie
B bit it
C cut it
D dealt it
E eat it
F fought for it

G got it
H had it
I investigated it
J joined it
K kept it
L longed for it

M	mourned for it	S	stole it
N	nodded at it	T	took it
O	opened it	U	upraised it
P	peeped in it	V	viewed it
Q	quartered it	W	wanted it
R	ran for it	X Y Z	& ampersand all wished for a piece in hand.

Little Polly Flinders
  Sat among the cinders
Warming her pretty little toes.
  Her mother came and caught
    her,
And whipped her little daughter
  For spoiling her nice new
    clothes.

Little Tommy Tucker
  Sings for his supper;
What shall we give him?
  White bread and butter.
How shall he cut it,
  Without e'er a knife?
How can he marry
  Without e'er a wife?

Little Boy Blue, come blow up
    your horn,
  The sheep's in the meadow, the
    cow's in the corn.
Where is the boy that looks after
    the sheep?
  He's under the haycock fast
    asleep!

From *Lavender's Blue; A Book of Nursery Rhymes*, compiled by Kathleen Lines, and published by Franklin Watts, Inc.

A PUSSYCAT'S CHRISTMAS

Margaret Wise Brown

You can actually hear, feel, and even smell this wonderful Christmas that came to a lovable little pussycat.

IT WAS Christmas.
  How could you tell?
Was the snow falling?

No.

The little cat Pussycat knew that
  Christmas was coming.

The ice tinkled when it broke on
  the frozen mud puddles.
The cold air made her hair stand
  straight up in the air.
And the air smelled just as it did
  last year.
What did it smell like?
Could she smell Christmas trees?
Of course she could.

6

And Tangerines? And Christmas
   Greens? And Holly?
And could she hear the crackle
   and slip of white tissue paper?
And red tissue paper?
She certainly could.
Tissue paper rustled
Nuts cracked
Scissors cut

Trees were chopped down
People shivered
And horses made funny noises,
Brrrrr.

There wasn't a flake of snow in
   the sky.
But the sky was dark and low and
   there was the dark smell of winter air before snow.

And then, *click,*
   the street lights clicked on all
   over the town.

Outside the house they lit the
   lights.
And as the heavens turned blue
   beyond the window,
one
by
one
the snowflakes began to fall out
   of the sky.

Sshshhhhhhhhssss

How did little Pussycat know?
Could she hear the snow?
She certainly could. And she ran
   right out into the snow storm.

For if there was anything that this
   little cat loved, it was the cold,
   dry, fresh, white, wild and
   feathery powdery snow.

7

She went pouncing around in it,
  bouncing around in awful joy.
And she ate some of it.
And she rolled in it and dug in it
  and played with it.
And then she stood up and stood
  all white with snow — *very still.*
For it was very quiet,
very quiet.

First there was no sound.
And then there was some.
For when everything is quiet, you
  can hear things far away.

From the sky with a sound like
  steady whispering came the
  snow —
— That sound of snow —
Snow that has never been on this
  earth before.

Then the wind rattled the black
  branches and rattled the time
  for Pussycat to go into the house.

For little cats do not like the wind.
  They usually don't like snow,
  but this little cat did.
All the smells of the earth that she
  knew were frozen and buried in
  the white snow. The world was
  very quiet and very mysterious
  without sound. Even footsteps
  were quiet. Pussycat didn't go
  in right away because through
  the wind and the falling snow
  she heard something.
She stood very still and stretched
  her ears there in the whitened
  darkness.

And soon she heard it coming
  from far away,
  away off up the snowy road.

8

Ding, ding, ding, ding,
Jingle, jingle, jingle, ding.
What was it?
She heard it going by in the white,
falling snow.

She saw it!

She saw the sleigh go jingling by.

Then Pussycat meowed at her windowpane. And she heard footsteps coming to let her in.
They always let her in right away
because they didn't want her to
get cold and they liked to have
her in the house.

She walked right into the living
room where she could smell the
sharp tangy smell of Christmas
trees and candles and nuts and
raisins and apples and tangerines.
But they wouldn't let her stay in
the living room where they
were wrapping up packages
and hanging things on a tree.

So they put her out in the hall and
closed the glass doors.
And this is why.
Pussycat pounced.

She pounced on everything.
And she waited to pounce with
shining eyes and switching tail.

She waited with shining eyes for
something to fall, to tinkle, to
crash and to break.
She batted the Christmas tree
balls with her paw.
Tore at the tissue paper
and pulled the bows off the packages.

Pussycat lay down in the wide
vast hall and put her nose in
front of herself and purred by
the fire.
She lifted her ears and she listened.
There was a sound of crackling.

Shhhhh Shhhhh Crackle
What was that?
Was it the fire?
Always there was the sound of
snow . . . . . . hissing against
the windowpane.

9

And snip, snip. Snip, snip.
Scissors were cutting string.
Then there was a tiny tinkly little
pop, as something fell from the
Christmas tree and shivered
into a million splinters of light.
That was wonderful.
The lights gleamed in Pussycat's
eyes.

Then bang, bang, bang.
What was that?
Someone was hanging the Christ-
mas stockings.
Hammering nails to hang the
Christmas stockings.

Everyone came out and stepped
over and around the little cat
and put on coats and boots and
mufflers and hats and laughed
and shuffled about.

They kissed each other under the
mistletoe.
Then off they went to Church.

Suddenly and quietly far off in the
night Pussycat could hear
Ding Dong Ding Dong
Ding Dong
Ding Dong Ding Dong
Ding Dong Ding Dong
Ding Dong
Ding Dong
Ding Dong
Ding Dong Ding Dong

When everyone had gone it was
dark and quiet. The snow had
stopped.
And there was only the smell of
the Christmas tree filling the
house.

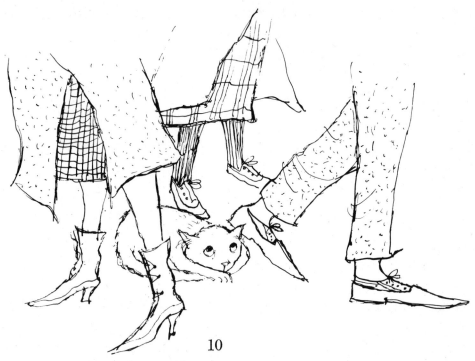

10

Silent Night
Holy Night
Child of Heav'n
O how bright
Thou dids't smile when Thou wast
   born
Blessed be that happy morn
Sleep in heavenly peace
Sleep in heavenly peace.

And silence.

Then softly at first but distinct in the night she heard people walking from window to window — the dark carolers on the white snow.

Through the still air their voices came to her listening ears — over the silence of the frozen snow — in the silence of the moonlight — in the silence of the night — in the silence of the bright stars in the sky.

Silent Night
Holy Night
All is calm
All is bright
Radiance gleams from heaven afar
Heavenly hosts sing Hallelujah
Sleep in heavenly peace
Sleep in heavenly peace.

And as the little Pussycat purred and purred by the fire, she heard in the distance the music fading far down the road.

Pussycat listened for a long time. Of course she didn't understand the words, but she liked the mystery of it all.

Then she pushed open the living room door with her paw and there in the silent house was the Christmas tree.

It sparkled and glistened with lights, gold and silver and blue, the light of rubies and emeralds, shining like no tree that any cat had ever seen in the woods.

This to Pussycat was Christmas Eve.

Conclusion:

   In the complete book *A Pussycat's Christmas*, by Margaret Wise Brown, published by Thomas Y. Crowell Company, you will find many delightful pictures about this story. Margaret Wise Brown has also written *The Runaway Bunny* and *Goodnight Moon*, both published by Harper & Brothers, and *The Golden Egg Book*, published by Simon and Schuster, Inc.

1, 2, Buckle my shoe;

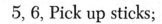

5, 6, Pick up sticks;

7, 8, Lay them straight;

3, 4, Knock at the door;

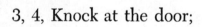

9, 10, A good fat hen.

11, 12, Dig and delve;

15, 16, Maids in the kitchen;
17, 18, Maids a-waiting;

13, 14, Maids a-courting;

19, 20, My plate's empty.

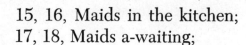

From *Lavender's Blue; A Book of Nursery Rhymes*, compiled by Kathleen Lines, and published by Franklin Watts, Inc.

Little Jack Horner
   Sat in a corner,
Eating a Christmas pie;
   He put in his thumb
And pulled out a plum,
   And said, What a good
Boy am I!

Mary, Mary, quite contrary,
   How does your garden grow?
With silver bells and cockle-shells,
   And pretty maids all in a row.

Here am I, little Jumping Joan.
   When nobody's with me,
I'm always alone.

A dillar, a dollar.
   A ten o'clock scholar.
What makes you come so soon?
   You used to come at ten o'clock,
But now you come at noon.

From *Lavender's Blue; A Book of Nursery Rhymes*,
compiled by Kathleen Lines, and published by
Franklin Watts, Inc.

15

THE FIVE CHINESE BROTHERS

Claire Huchet Bishop

Surely you have never heard of five such fascinating brothers or of five such amazing gifts. Why, one of the brothers could even swallow the sea!

ONCE UPON A TIME there were Five Chinese Brothers and they all looked exactly alike.

They lived with their mother in a little house not far from the sea.

The First Chinese Brother could swallow the sea.

The Second Chinese Brother had an iron neck.

The Third Chinese Brother could stretch and stretch and stretch his legs.

The Fourth Chinese Brother could not be burned.

And

The Fifth Chinese Brother could hold his breath indefinitely.

Every morning the First Chinese Brother would go fishing, and whatever the weather, he would come back to the village with beautiful and rare fish which he had caught and could sell at the market for a very good price.

One day, as he was leaving the market place, a little boy stopped him and asked him if he could go fishing with him.

"No, it could not be done," said the First Chinese Brother.

But the little boy begged and begged and finally the First Chinese Brother consented. "Under one condition," said he, "and that is that you shall obey me promptly."

"Yes, yes," the little boy promised.

Early next morning, the First Chinese Brother and the little boy went down to the beach.

"Remember," said the First Chinese Brother, "you must obey me promptly. When I make a sign for you to come back, you must come at once."

"Yes, yes," the little boy promised.

Then the First Chinese Brother swallowed the sea.

And all the fish were left high and dry at the bottom of the sea. And all the treasures of the sea lay uncovered.

The little boy was delighted. He ran here and there stuffing his pockets with strange pebbles, extraordinary shells and fantastic algae.

Near the shore the First Chinese Brother gathered some fish while holding the sea in his mouth. Presently he grew tired. It is very hard to hold the sea. So he made a sign with his hand for the little boy to come back. The little boy saw him but paid no attention.

The First Chinese Brother made great movements with his arms

17

that meant "Come back!" But did the little boy care? Not a bit and he ran further away.

Then the First Chinese Brother felt the sea swelling inside him and he made desperate gestures to call the little boy back. But the little boy made faces at him and fled as fast as he could.

The First Chinese Brother held the sea until he thought he was going to burst. All of a sudden the sea forced its way out of his mouth, went back to its bed . . .

and the little boy disappeared.

When the First Chinese Brother returned to the village, alone, he was arrested, put in prison, tried and condemned to have his head cut off.

On the morning of the execution he said to the judge:

"Your Honor, will you allow me to go and bid my mother good-bye?"

"It is only fair," said the judge.

So the First Chinese Brother went home . . . and the Second Chinese Brother came back in his place.

18

All the people were assembled on the village square to witness the execution. The executioner took his sword and struck a mighty blow.

But the Second Chinese Brother got up and smiled. He was the one with the iron neck and they simply could not cut his head off. Everybody was angry and they decided that he should be drowned.

On the morning of the execution, the Second Chinese Brother said to the judge:

19

"Your Honor, will you allow me to go and bid my mother good-bye?"

"It is only fair," said the judge.

So the Second Chinese Brother went home . . . and the Third Chinese Brother came back in his place.

He was pushed on a boat which made for the open sea.

When they were far out on the ocean, the Third Chinese Brother was thrown overboard.

But he began to stretch and stretch and stretch his legs, way down to the bottom of the sea, and all the time his smiling face was bobbing up and down on the crest of the waves. He simply could not be drowned.

Everybody was very angry, and they all decided that he should be burned.

On the morning of the execution, the Third Chinese Brother said to the judge:

"Your Honor, will you allow me to go and bid my mother good-bye?"

"It is only fair," said the judge. So the Third Chinese Brother went home . . . and the Fourth Chinese Brother came back in his place.

He was tied up to a stake. Fire was set to it and all the people stood around watching it. In the midst of the flames they heard him say:

"This is quite pleasant."

"Bring some more wood!" the people cried.

The fire roared higher.

"Now it is quite comfortable," said the Fourth Chinese Brother, for he was the one who could not be burned. Everybody was getting more and more angry every

21

minute and they all decided to smother him.

On the morning of the execution, the Fourth Chinese Brother said to the judge:

"Your Honor, will you allow me to go and bid my mother good-bye?"

"It is only fair," said the judge.

So the Fourth Chinese Brother went home . . . and the Fifth Chinese Brother came back in his place. A large brick oven had been built on the village square and it had been all stuffed with whipped cream. The Fifth Chinese Brother was shovelled into the oven, right in the middle of the cream, the door was shut tight, and everybody sat around and waited.

They were not going to be tricked again! So they stayed there all night and even a little after dawn, just to make sure.

Then they opened the door and pulled him out. And he shook himself and said, "My! That was a good sleep!"

Everybody stared open-mouthed and round-eyed. But the judge stepped forward and said, "We have tried to get rid of you in every possible way and somehow it cannot be done. It must be that you are innocent."

"Yes, yes," shouted all the people. So they let him go and he went home.

And the Five Chinese Brothers and their mother all lived together happily for many years.

Conclusion:

For many amusing colored pictures about this story, you must consult the book *The Five Chinese Brothers*, by Claire Huchet Bishop, published by Coward-McCann, Inc. Mrs. Bishop has also written books for older boys and girls, among them *Twenty and Ten* and *Pancakes — Paris*, both published by The Viking Press.

LUNCHTIME AT
THE ZOO

Ilo Orleans

"It's time for lunch,"
The zoo-keeper said;
"And what would you like today?"
Jumbo, the elephant,
Trumpeted loud:
"Peanuts, and lettuce, and hay!"

"Now, Mister Sea-lion,"
The zoo-keeper called,
"Tell me, what is *your* wish?"
The sea-lion blinked,
Then happily barked,
"My wish is a pailful of fish!"

"And *you*, Mister Hippo?"
The zoo-keeper asked,
"I'll open my mouth!" Hippo cried,
"And, please, won't you toss
A basket of bread,
And a bucket of apples, inside!"

THE KANGAROO

Ilo Orleans

Today when I was at the zoo,
I watched the mother kangaroo.
Inside her skin she has a pocket.
She puts her baby there to rock it.

BABY LLAMA

Ilo Orleans

Do you think
  A baby Llama
Ever calls
  Its mother, "Mama?"

23

SILENT GIRAFFE

Ilo Orleans

Isn't it
Amazing —
With such a long, long throat,
The tall giraffe
Can't make a sound —
And cannot sing a note!

FLIPPERS

Ilo Orleans

Flapping his flippers,
The barking seal
Cries: "I want fish
For my noonday meal."

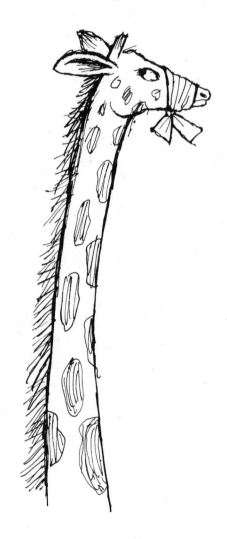

ICE-BATHER

Ilo Orleans

A polar bear
   Believes it's nice
To take a bath
   In a pool of ice!

TRUCKS

James S. Tippett

Big trucks for steel beams,
Big trucks for coal,
Rumbling down the broad streets,
Heavily they roll.

Little trucks for groceries,
Little trucks for bread,
Turning into every street,
Rushing on ahead.

Big trucks, little trucks,
In never-ending lines,
Rumble on and rush ahead
While I read their signs.

From *I Go A-Traveling*, by James S. Tippett, published by Harper & Brothers.

TRAINS

James S. Tippett

Over the mountains,
Over the plains,
Over the rivers,
Here come the trains.

25

Carrying passengers,
Carrying mail,
Bringing their precious loads
In without fail.

Thousands of freight cars
All rushing on
Through day and darkness,
Through dusk and dawn.

Over the mountains,
Over the plains,
Over the rivers,
Here come the trains.

From *I Go A-Traveling*, by James S. Tippett, published by Harper & Brothers.

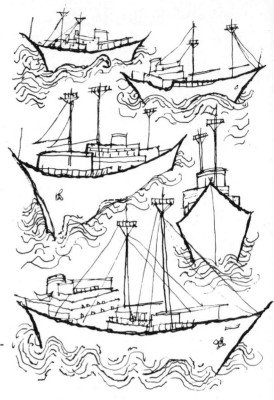

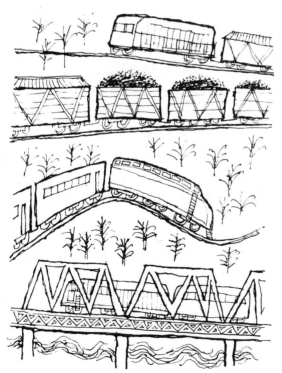

FREIGHT BOATS

James S. Tippett

Boats that carry sugar
And tobacco from Havana;
Boats that carry coconuts
And coffee from Brazil;
Boats that carry cotton
From the city of Savannah;
Boats that carry anything
From any place you will.

Boats like boxes loaded down
With tons of sand and gravel;
Boats with blocks of granite

For a building on the hill;
Boats that measure many thousand
Lonesome miles of travel
As they carry anything
From any place you will.

From *I Go A-Traveling*, by James S. Tippett, published by Harper & Brothers.

UP IN THE AIR

James S. Tippett

Zooming across the sky,
Like a great bird you fly.
    Airplane,
    Silvery white
    In the light.

Turning and twisting in air,
When shall I ever be there.
    Airplane,
    Piloting you
    Far in the blue?

From *I Go A-Traveling*, by James S. Tippett, published by Harper & Brothers.

DRINKING FOUNTAIN

Marchette Chute

When I climb up
    To get a drink,
It doesn't work
    The way you'd think.

I turn it up.
    The water goes
And hits me right
    Upon the nose.

I turn it down
    To make it small
And don't get any
    Drink at all.

From *Around and About,* by Marchette Chute, published by E. P. Dutton & Co., Inc.

THE TEA PARTY

Marchette Chute

I had a new tea set
    Just given to me,
So I asked Priscilla
    To come and have tea.

Cook made us cookies
    And iced them with pink,
And fixed us some milk
    With real tea in to drink.

The teapot was ready
    And filled to the brim,
With a row of pink roses
    Encircling the rim.

So we sat in the garden
    Under a tree,
Both in pink dresses,
    And had a pink tea.

From *Around and About,* by Marchette Chute, published by E. P. Dutton & Co., Inc.

THE PRETZEL MAN

Rachel Field

The Pretzel Man has a little stand
With spikes like the fingers on a
    hand,

28

And every one strung up and
    down
With rings all baked to crispy
    brown.
The very richest queens and kings
Could never wear so many rings;
Though theirs be made of bright-
    est gold
Set thick with jewels ages old —
Still, Pretzel Men can *eat* their
    rings
And this is not the case with kings!

From *Taxis and Toadstools*, by Rachel Field, published by Doubleday & Company, Inc.

VEGETABLES
Rachel Field

A carrot has a green fringed top;
A beet is royal red;

And lettuces are curious
All curled and run to head.

Some beans have strings to tie
    them on,
And, what is still more queer,
Ripe corn is nothing more or less
Than one enormous ear!

But when potatoes all have eyes,
Why is it they should be
Put in the ground and covered
    up —
Where it's too dark to see?

From *Taxis and Toadstools*, by Rachel Field, published by Doubleday & Company, Inc.

MARGARET
Tom Robinson

I have a baby sister,
Who rolls around the floor
And when I tell her not to roll,
She just rolls some more.

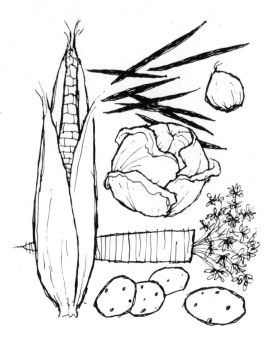

She rolls to east, she rolls to west,
She rolls to north and south.
She chuckles as she rolls around,
Her wee fist in her mouth.

Roly-poly Margaret,
Rolling on the floor —
Till she gets tired, tuckered out,
And can't roll any more.

From *In and Out,* by Tom Robinson, published by The Viking Press.

SNEAKERS COMES TO TOWN

Margaret Wise Brown

Sneakers is a fat little cat, inky black except for his four white paws. When he was very tiny, his mother used to lick and lick his feet to try and get the white off. Her other kittens were black all over, and she couldn't understand why this one should have white feet. And then one day she saw the little boy running around in a pair of brand-new clean white sneakers. From then on the little cat was called Sneakers.

ALL SUMMER Sneakers went prowling around and prowling around on his sneaker-white paws.

And he grew from a kitten to a cat.

But he was only a small cat, the size of a large kitten.

And he was still the little boy's cat, and he was still a rapscallion cat.

When the little boy caught a fish in the river and pulled it up on the bank, *pounce* went Sneakers on the wiggling fish.

When the cook's feet went walking by one of Sneaker's hiding places, *pounce* came Sneakers, *pounce* at the walking feet.

And at night he went *pounce* to sleep on all the best chairs in the house.

He was a rapscallion cat, but the little boy loved him.

And he was the little boy's cat.

Then one day at the end of summer the whole house packed up to go to the city for the winter.

The cook packed her feather hat.

The little boy's mother packed the straw hats and all the silver and all the summer clothes.

And she packed the little boy's shorts, and sandals, and sneakers, and socks, and all his clothes.

The little boy's father packed all his pipes and tobacco, and his fishing rods, and all his clothes.

And then they all got in the car with the suitcases to drive to town.

The little boy was very sad.

Sneakers couldn't go.

His mother said the city was no place for an animal.

Sneakers couldn't go.

His father said that all animals belonged in the country.

Sneakers couldn't go.

He would have to wait all winter for the little boy to come back.

So, before the car drove off, the little boy jumped out to tell Sneakers good-bye.

He called Sneakers, but the little cat didn't come.

He looked all through the house.

He looked in the cellar.

He looked in the barn.

And he looked in the field behind the barn.

No Sneakers.

So the little boy just called out across the field, "Good-bye, Sneakers, my rapscallion cat."

Then he went back to the car, and the car drove off to the city.

He didn't see Sneakers to tell him good-bye.

When they got to the city, they drove to a red brick house on 15th Street.

There was a very small garden in front of it, behind a high, black, iron fence.

The garden was the size of a very, very small rug.

It wasn't even big enough to start to run in without bumping into the big iron fence.

But Sneakers wasn't there, and the little boy didn't want to run anyway.

His mother and his father went into the house.

His mother unpacked the silver.

His father unpacked his tobacco and his pipes.

And then his mother began to open the suitcases.

First she opened the suitcase with the little boy's toys in it.

Some nuts and sticks fell out and rolled all over the floor and under the bed.

Then she opened the suitcase with all of his father's clothes in it.

She unpacked them and hung them up on wooden hangers.

Then she opened her own suitcase and hung up all her dresses.

Then she opened the little boy's suitcase and . . . Wait! What in the world?

Out pounced a little black bundle of fur that jumped up on the bed.

It was Sneakers!

Sneakers, purring and purring, and arching his back.

He meowed just once when the little boy ran up to him.

"Oh, that Sneakers!" said the little boy's mother.

"That rapscallion cat!"

"How in the world did he ever get in that suitcase?"

"He must have fallen asleep there," said the little boy's father,

"and we didn't see him when we closed the bag.

"Lucky he didn't smother, that bad little cat."

And he puffed on his pipe, but his eyes were smiling.

The little boy didn't say a thing.

He just scratched Sneakers on the nose.

Sneakers batted the little boy's hand with his white sneaker paw.

"What will we ever do in the city with a rapscallion cat?" said the little boy's mother.

"We had better send him back to the country."

"No," said the little boy's father, "if he has come this far by himself, let him stay."

So the little cat stayed in the city with the little boy.

Conclusion:

This lovable little kitten has more adventures in a book *Sneakers,* by Margaret Wise Brown, published by William R. Scott, Inc. In one, he finds the sea. In another, he has an Easter surprise.

BETSY GOES TO SCHOOL AND FINDS A BIG SURPRISE

Carolyn Haywood

Six-year-old Betsy was not at all sure she was going to like school. Even the beautiful plaid school-bag and all the other nice things could not keep her from thinking how strange it was to be going to school. But soon everything was different. Exciting and interesting things began to happen.

BETSY lay in her little white bed. She had been awake a long time. Outside her window the birds were calling "Good morning" to each other, but Betsy did not hear them.

33

All summer long she had jumped out of bed as soon as her eyes were open. She had always run to the window and thrown sunflower seeds out to the birds for their breakfast. But this morning Betsy was so busy feeling unhappy that she forgot all about the birds.

Betsy was unhappy because today was the first day of school. She had never been to school and she was sure she would not like it. Old Ned, who cut the grass on Grandfather's farm, had told her all about school. Betsy had never told anyone what Old Ned had told her, but now she lay thinking about it. She thought of the cross old teacher and of the switch that had stood in the corner to be used on the legs of any child who might be late for school. She thought of the high pointed cap made of paper that Old Ned had been made to wear when he didn't know his spelling. Old Ned had stroked his grizzly beard and said, "Aye, yes! School was a terrible place."

Betsy turned her head on the pillow. Now she could see her clothes lying on her bedroom chair. There was her new green dress with the little puffy pockets. It was such a pretty dress but Betsy wished that she did not have to go to school in it. She leaned far over the side of her bed to see if she could see her new shoes. There they were, side by side, little brown shoes that fastened with a strap and a brass buckle. And there, hanging on the doorknob, was her school-bag. It was dark green with red and yellow stripes running up and down and across it. Mother called it plaid. It was trimmed with bright red and there was a long leather strap that Betsy could hang over her shoulder. Betsy had been happy the day Father had bought the bag for her. But now that the time had come for her to wear it she didn't feel happy at all. If only she could run away and hide!

Just then Mother came in. "Come, Betsy, it's time to get up," said Mother. "Today you are going to school."

Mother helped her with her bath and brushed and braided her hair. Then she tied the crisp white sash on her dress.

After breakfast, Mother went upstairs to put on her hat. She was going to walk to school with Betsy every morning until Betsy knew the way.

Betsy sat on the bottom step of the stairs to wait for Mother. Her school-bag was over her shoulder. There were two bread and jelly sandwiches tucked away in the pocket on the outside of the bag. Betsy felt very little and very scared, but she wouldn't tell Mother, because she did not want Mother to think that she was a baby. Only that morning Mother had called her "Mother's great big girl."

Suddenly Betsy thought of

Koala Bear. Koala was the little toy bear that Uncle Jim had brought all the way from Australia. She would take Koala to school with her. It would not seem so strange or so lonely with Koala. Betsy ran upstairs and into her bedroom. She looked in the bed, but Koala was not there. Betsy was sure she had taken him to bed with her the night before. She pulled up the covers at the foot of the bed, for although Koala always went to bed with his nose sticking out at the top, it was nearly always sticking out at the bottom of the bed in the morning. Sometimes he even fell out completely. Betsy looked under the bed and around the floor, but there was no Koala. She looked on the window sill and in

the toy closet, but Koala was no-where to be seen.

"Betsy," called Mother from the foot of the stairs, "come at once, dear. You mustn't be late for school."

Betsy took one last look in the bed, but there was no sign of a little gray bear. Very slowly she went downstairs.

"I can't find Koala, Mother," said Betsy.

"Well, never mind Koala now," replied Mother. "He'll turn up; he always does."

Betsy took hold of Mother's hand, and they started on the long walk to school. Mother took such big long steps that Betsy had to take little skipping steps to keep

36

up with her. Every time she skipped she could hear her two pencils rattle in the pencil box inside her school-bag.

As they drew near the school, they saw a great many little boys and girls. They were coming from all directions. Some were with their mothers. Others were with big brothers and sisters. Betsy wondered whether all of the new little boys and girls were as frightened as she was.

At last they reached the school. Up the wide stone steps went Betsy, holding tightly to Mother's hand. In a little room a lady wearing glasses wrote Betsy's name on a pink card.

"Come this way, Betsy," said the lady with the glasses. She opened a door and Mother and Betsy passed into a room full of boys and girls. Each one was sitting behind a little brown desk.

A young lady with pale yellow hair shook hands with Mother. "This is Miss Grey, who will be Betsy's teacher," said the lady with the glasses.

"Good morning, Betsy," said Miss Grey.

"Good morning," said Betsy, as Mother quietly slipped out the door.

Betsy was alone now in a strange new place. What a big room it was! One whole side of the

room was made of windows. They were the biggest windows Betsy had ever seen. The walls seemed so far away and parts of them were black. In some places there was writing on the black walls. And the ceiling — how high it was! It looked way, way off. So this was school! This great big room with the black walls and all the little desks was school. This was where she would have to come every morning. Betsy blinked her eyes to keep back the tears.

Miss Grey led her to a desk by the windows. It seemed such a long way from the door to the little desk. It seemed much longer than the whole way she had walked with Mother.

"This will be your desk, Betsy," said Miss Grey.

Betsy took off her school-bag and sat down. She thought of Mother who was getting farther and farther away every moment. "If I got up now and ran out the door," thought Betsy, "I could catch Mother. I could be out in the sunshine again with Mother and take hold of her hand. I could tell Mother that I don't want to go to school, that I know it is a terrible place, Old Ned said so." But Betsy knew that she couldn't do that. She knew that Mother would bring her back again and would be ashamed of her. Nothing could be done about it. She would have to stay. Two big tears began to roll down Betsy's cheeks. She felt in her pocket for her handkerchief. It was not there. Then Betsy remembered that Mother had put it in her school-bag. Betsy opened the bag and took out her shiny black pencil box. She felt for her handkerchief. As she did so, her hand touched something soft and furry. Betsy looked inside the bag and there, looking at her with bright beady eyes, was Koala Bear. Tied around his neck was one of Father's old red neckties, so Betsy knew that Father must have hidden Koala in her school-bag. Betsy wanted to hug him up tight, but instead she just put her hand in the bag and gave Koala a little squeeze and whispered, "Oh, Koala! I'm so glad to see you."

Betsy was so surprised to see Koala that she forgot all about her handkerchief and when she did think of it she found that she didn't need it after all.

Conclusion:

The book *"B" Is for Betsy,* by Carolyn Haywood, published by Harcourt, Brace and Company, from which this story is taken, tells about Betsy's entire first year at school. There are many other books by the same author about Betsy and her friends Billy and Ellen.

IT'S FUN TO SLIDE ON THE BANISTER
Carolyn Haywood

Six-year-old Teddy and his little sister Babs lived in a big apartment house behind a door that had "11-A" on it. They had to take an elevator to get to the street. One day Daddy came home and said: "We are moving to a farm." Now Teddy and Babs no longer use an elevator, but they don't always walk down the stairs either.

TEDDY AND BABS loved the farm. There was the stone house to live in and there was a big barn and a stable. The house seemed very big to Teddy and Babs after living in the apartment, and it had a great many doors and windows. The driveway led up to a white door with a shiny brass knocker, but there were stepping-stones that led around to the other side of the house and there was a porch and another white door. This door had a bell that you pulled.

Teddy and Babs couldn't agree about the front door. Teddy said that the door with the knocker was the front door, and Babs said that the door with the bell was the front door. When they asked Daddy about it, he said, "Let's have two front doors. After all, anybody can have one front door, but it is very special to have two front doors." So they called them "the knocker front door" and "the bell front door." There was a side door too and a back door, and pretty soon

there were toys beside every door. Finally Daddy fell over them once too often and then he built a closet under the stairs. It was called "the toy stable" and Teddy and Babs had to put their toys in the stable when they were through playing with them.

Teddy and Babs thought the stairs were the nicest part of the house for they had never had stairs before. The stairs were long because the ceilings were very high and it took a great many steps to reach from the first floor to the second floor. Of course with so many steps there was a long banister rail and Teddy and Babs thought this was the most fun of all. They sat on the banister at the top and slid down to the bottom over and over again. Sometimes they slid down separately and sometimes they slid down together. Sometimes they came down backwards and sometimes frontwards and every once in a while they discovered a new way to slide down the banister. Sometimes Daddy or Mother would say, "No, no! Not that way," and Teddy and Babs would have to give up their brand-new discovery.

Teddy and Babs spent hours playing on the stairs. There were so many games to play. Sometimes they were animals in the zoo and they looked out between the bars and roared terrible roars. Sometimes they made believe that the stairs was a hill and they tobogganed down to the bottom. Sometimes it was a train with dolls and stuffed animals traveling to the city, but Teddy and Babs agreed that the most fun was to slide down the banister.

One day the painter came to paint the woodwork in the hall. He painted all of the posts white, and the banister he painted a beautiful dark brown. When the painter went home at the end of the day, it looked so beautiful and clean that Mother was delighted. "Now remember," she said to Teddy and Babs, "you must be very careful not to touch the wet paint. It takes two days for the paint to dry."

Teddy and Babs said that they would remember and trotted off to bed.

The next morning when they came downstairs, Babs said, "Don't touch the paint, Teddy. It's wet."

"I know it's wet," said Teddy. "You don't have to tell me."

After breakfast, Mother said, "Who wants to go to the village with me to get the mail at the post office?"

"I do! I do!" cried Babs.

"Are you coming too, Teddy?" asked Mother.

"No," replied Teddy. "I'm very busy. I'm building an airport for my airplanes."

Mother and Babs drove off and left Teddy alone. After a while he went upstairs to get a piece of string that was in his little desk drawer. He stuck the string in his

pocket and trotted off. "This is a wonderful airport that I am building," thought Teddy. "Mother and Babs will be surprised when they come home and see what I have made. And I'll keep it to show to Daddy too."

When he reached the head of the stairs, Teddy threw his little leg over the banister and "Zoop!" down he went to the bottom. There he stopped. Instead of getting off as he always did, he sat very still. Something was the matter and the matter was that Teddy was stuck. He was stuck to the banister. He looked at his hands. His palms were covered with brown paint. He looked at the banister. All the way down the banister there was a light streak where Teddy had wiped off the paint. Very carefully he pulled himself loose. There was a sticky noise as though the banister didn't want to let Teddy go. His blue linen trousers felt very wet and sticky, for all the paint that had been on the banister was now on the seat of his little trousers.

Teddy went upstairs to the bathroom. He washed his hands with soap. He rubbed them very hard, but they stayed dark brown. Then he took off his trousers. Out of his bureau drawer he took another pair of blue linen trousers

just like the ones he had spoiled. He put them on and buttoned them to his white shirt. Then he picked up the painty trousers and hid them on the floor of the closet, way back in the corner where it was very dark.

As he went down the stairs he looked at the banister. "It doesn't show very much," thought Teddy. "Maybe Mother won't see it."

Somehow, he didn't want to go on building his airport. Something made him want to get out of doors and away from the house. So, without telling Mary, the cook, where he was going, he ran down the hill and across the meadow to the

brook. There he floated leaves and sticks and made believe they were boats racing.

After a while, Mother and Babs came home. Mother went upstairs to take off her things. She looked at the banister and she saw the streak running from the top to the bottom and she saw the finger marks but she didn't say anything.

It was almost lunch time when Teddy came back to the house. "Hello, Teddy," said Mother, "did you have a nice morning?"

"Uh-huh," murmured Teddy.

"Did you finish your airport?" asked Babs.

"No, I didn't," replied Teddy.

When lunch was ready, Mother said, "Teddy, are your hands clean? Let me look at them."

Teddy turned his palms upward. They were still very brown.

"My goodness!" said Mother, "what dirty hands!"

"They get awful dirty playing around," said Teddy.

"They certainly do," replied Mother. "Go and wash them."

Teddy washed his hands. Again he rubbed them very, very hard and he used a great deal of soap, but it was no use. They were still brown.

He slid into his place at the table and kept his fists clenched all through lunch.

"Why didn't you finish your airport?" asked Mother.

"Oh, I just didn't want to," replied Teddy.

As soon as lunch was over, he ran back to the brook. He spent the afternoon building a dam out of stones.

43

Babs played with her dolls on the living-room floor. Once she said, "Mother, I wonder where Teddy is."

"I wonder!" replied Mother.

Late in the afternoon the painter returned. He painted the banister all over again with dark brown paint. Then he put a big sign at the top of the stairs and a big sign at the bottom of the stairs. The signs said, "Wet Paint."

Teddy came back just before dinner. He was very quiet.

That night when Mother gave him his bath, Teddy wondered why Mother scrubbed the place where the seat of his trousers went so very hard. She had never scrubbed him so hard there before, and she used a great deal of soap. After he was all dry, he put on his pajamas. Mother heard him say his

prayers. He jumped into bed and Mother tucked the covers all around him. Then she sat down on the edge of his bed.

"Teddy," she said, "isn't there something that you would like to tell Mother?"

Teddy was very quiet. He was quiet a long time. Mother sat waiting. She hummed a little tune.

At last Teddy said, "I didn't do it on purpose, Mother. I just forgot about the paint and when I remembered I was down at the bottom."

"I see," said Mother. "Is there anything else?"

"Yes," said Teddy, "my trousers are on the closet floor, way back in the corner."

"I'll get them," said Mother. "I'm glad you told me, Teddy." And she kissed her little boy goodnight.

Conclusion:

On the Fourth of July Teddy and Babs go on a picnic. On another day they find a buried treasure. All these stories are in the book *Two and Two Are Four,* by Carolyn Haywood, published by Harcourt, Brace and Company.

THE HOMESICK TREE

Miriam E. Mason

Sarah Samantha Glossbrenner was a very timid little girl who lived back in the days when many families were moving westward. She thought the lion's tooth which hung from Uncle Romeo's watch chain might help her to be brave. Uncle Romeo promised to give it to her when she made him a dumpling with apples picked from her own young tree. When the family moved west, Sarah Samantha and big sister Miney and little sister Annie took "Miss Appleseed" along and planted her at the new homestead. But something was wrong — Miss Appleseed didn't seem happy!

THE NEXT MORNING Mr. Glossbrenner planted the apple tree in the place Sarah Samantha had chosen.

He dug a deep hole for Miss Appleseed's roots. Sarah Samantha took off the old horse blanket and the straw. She helped to put the tree in place and cover up the roots.

She brought a bucket of water and poured it on the tree.

"Now you are at home," she said to Miss Appleseed.

Every day she hunted for buds on the little tree, and hoped to see green apples growing. She was pleased to notice leaves on the tree.

But after a few days the apple tree did not seem so well. No more buds came. The leaves did not grow bigger. Some of them dried up and soon fell off.

"I do wonder what is the matter with Miss Appleseed," thought Sarah Samantha when she looked out at the tree.

"Perhaps the tree is thirsty," said Mrs. Glossbrenner.

The days were getting warm now, and the weather was dry.

Sarah Samantha thought of the brook back in Ohio. She wished she might see the brook again and go wading in it.

45

"I do wish we had a nice brook on our homestead," she said to Miney as she helped her wash the dishes one warm day. "It would be fun to go wading in the brook. The water feels so comfortable to your bare feet!"

"Here we have a river!" said Miney proudly as she scrubbed a big skillet. "A river is bigger than a brook. And a homestead is bigger than a farm!"

"Sometimes I get tired of so much bigness!" said Sarah Samantha as she looked out the door.

As far as she could see, there was only the homestead.

"You may have the dishwater for your apple tree," Miney told her sister as they finished the dishes.

People on a homestead did not waste water. Water was scarce and had to be carried to the house. Water which had been used for washing dishes or taking a bath was still useful.

Sarah Samantha carried the pan of dishwater out and poured it around the roots of the apple tree. The water was soapy and looked dull.

"I would not like a drink of soapy dishwater no matter how thirsty I felt," thought Sarah Samantha. It seemed to her that Miss Appleseed looked smaller and more dried up than she did yesterday. "I think you are homesick!" said Sarah Samantha to the little tree. "The homestead is so big and so strange, and dishwater has such a disagreeable taste."

She wondered how to keep Miss Appleseed from being homesick. At last she decided to bring fresh water from the river for the tree to drink.

"Annie can walk along with me for company," she thought. "It will be a nice little walk for both of us."

Little Annie was glad to go with Sarah Samantha to get water. She had to walk slowly, and she sometimes fell down; for she was a very small girl.

But she talked and laughed and was cheerful. She listened and laughed when Sarah Samantha told her interesting stories about brave people.

Sometimes gophers came out of their holes and looked at the girls walking toward the river. Gophers are animals which live in holes in the ground in the prairie country.

The gophers had sharp faces with small bright eyes and very long front teeth. They looked like big rats, Sarah Samantha thought. She always felt like running when she saw a gopher looking out at her from his hole.

But of course she could not run away from Annie, who poked along on her fat little legs. She could not run with a bucket of water in her hand.

She had to walk slowly past the gopher holes and pretend that she was not afraid of gophers or snakes or any of the wild creatures around the homestead.

"Someday when I have my lion's tooth, I am going to walk up to a gopher hole and look right in at the gopher. How scared he will be to see my eyes staring at him!"

But, even with all the buckets of water, Miss Appleseed still seemed a little homesick. One time when Sarah Samantha was pouring the water on the tree's roots she saw some tiny toothmarks on the bark of the tree.

She told her father about this, and he thought awhile. Then he made a little fence all around Miss Appleseed. It was made of tiny poles pounded into the ground. They were so close together that nothing could get in between them.

"Now Miss Appleseed has a little picket fence just like we had around our old home back in Ohio!" he said.

Sarah Samantha painted the small picket fence with whitewash, and it looked just beautiful.

Soon Miss Appleseed began to grow. New leaves and buds came on her branches. She grew taller.

"She is not homesick any more," thought Sarah Samantha happily. "With fresh water to drink, and a picket fence around her, she feels at home."

Conclusion:

Miss Appleseed meets many other dangers in the book *The Middle Sister,* by Miriam E. Mason, published by The Macmillan Company. One time it's grasshoppers that cause the trouble; another time it's pigs. Meanwhile, Sarah Samantha dreams of the apple dumpling she hopes to bake for Uncle Romeo.

THE RUNAWAY PONY
Clyde Robert Bulla

In the city apartment where he lived, Danny loved to play cowboy. He rode a chair for a horse and roped a footstool for a calf and had lots of fun pretending he lived on a ranch. And then one wonderful day Danny goes to visit on a real ranch! He goes along with his new friend, Slim, on the daily rounds and learns what a live cowboy's life is actually like.

IN THE MORNING Danny ate breakfast with Uncle Mack, Aunt Betty, and six cowboys.

One of the cowboys was called Slim. He had red hair and freckles. He grinned at Danny.

"Guess we're going to have a new cowboy on Bar-K Ranch," he said.

"Yes," said Uncle Mack. "I'm going to teach him to ride today."

48

After breakfast the cowboys carried their dishes to the kitchen. Danny carried his dishes to the kitchen, too. Then the cowboys rode away to work.

Danny and Uncle Mack went out to the bunkhouse.

"This is where the cowboys sleep," said Uncle Mack.

There were bunk beds along the wall. On the floor were rugs made of the skins of deer, bears, and mountain lions. Saddles, bridles, and ropes hung from pegs on the wall.

Uncle Mack took down a small saddle.

"This will be yours," he said.

They went to the stable. There were horses in some of the stalls. Some of them were eating out of the feedboxes.

"I like this black horse," said Danny.

"His name is Nip," said Uncle Mack. "He is my horse."

"I like this gray horse," said Danny.

"His name is Tuck," said Uncle Mack. "He is your Aunt Betty's horse."

Danny saw a pony. He was white with brown spots.

"I like this spotted pony," he said.

"His name is Ginger," said Uncle Mack. "He is going to be your horse."

Danny rubbed the pony's nose. "You're going to be my horse. I'm going to ride you and feed you and take care of you."

Ginger opened his mouth and made a funny little noise. It sounded like "Whee-ee!" He rubbed his nose on Danny's hand.

"I know what he wants," said Uncle Mack. "He wants some sugar."

Danny ran to the house. "Aunt Betty, may I have some sugar for Ginger?"

"I'll bring some when I come," said Aunt Betty. "I'm coming out to see you ride."

Danny went back to the stable. Uncle Mack showed him how to put the bridle over Ginger's head and slip the bit into his mouth. He showed him how to saddle Ginger and lead him out of the stable.

"Ginger is a good pony," said Uncle Mack. "He is strong, he can run fast, and he is gentle. Do you want to get on him now?"

Danny put his foot in the stirrup. It was easy to swing himself into the saddle.

"A cowboy sits straight in the saddle," Uncle Mack told him.

"Like this?" asked Danny.

"Yes. Straight, but not stiff. He rides with his legs straight down, and he doesn't bounce around in the saddle."

Aunt Betty came out. She had a white sugar sack in her hand. "There is some sugar in the bottom," she said. "You can give it to the pony."

She held up the sack. The wind was blowing. It took the sack out of her hand and blew it straight into the pony's face.

The pony jumped and ran.

"Whoa!" shouted Danny.

Ginger didn't stop.

Danny pulled on the reins. Ginger kept on running. He was running away.

Down across the pasture he went, as fast as the wind. Danny's hat blew off.

"Whoa!" he shouted.

There were bushes ahead. Danny thought Ginger was going to jump over them. But the pony stopped short. Danny went flying into the air and landed in the bushes.

He lay there a little while. He felt his arms and legs. He wasn't hurt, but he was out of breath.

Uncle Mack came riding up on his black horse. "Danny, are you all right?"

"Yes, I'm all right." Danny rubbed his legs as he came out of the bushes. "I thought you said Ginger was gentle."

"He is," said Uncle Mack, "but when the sugar sack hit him in the face, he didn't know what it was. It made him afraid, so he ran away."

Ginger was standing close to the bushes. Danny went over to him. The pony was not afraid now.

"Do you see why a cowboy wears boots with high heels?" asked Uncle Mack.

Danny shook his head.

"The heels keep his feet from going through the stirrups," said Uncle Mack. "If one of your feet

50

had gone through the stirrup, it might have caught there. You might have been dragged until you were hurt. As it is, you're not hurt at all, are you, Danny?"

"No," said Danny, "but I lost my hat."

"We'll pick it up on the way back," said Uncle Mack.

Danny got on the pony. He and Uncle Mack rode back to the stable together.

"Will I be a cowboy as soon as I learn to ride?" asked Danny.

"A cowboy has to ride," said Uncle Mack, "but he has to do other things, too."

That night Danny wrote another letter.

Dear Mother and Father:
     Today I rode a pony. He ran away, I fell off. I was not hurt. I like to ride, but I am not a cowboy yet.

                 Your son,
                 DANNY

Conclusion:

In the book *Surprise for a Cowboy,* by Clyde Robert Bulla, published by Thomas Y. Crowell Company, Danny rescues a lost calf, puts out a grass fire, and does many other interesting things on the ranch. After each adventure he writes a letter home.

THE ENEMY
Irmengarde Eberle

The favorite place of Suzie and Peter and Mark was the garden house of the house next door. Since no one lived next door, it was almost as if they owned the favorite place. Mr. Pell, the real owner, had told them they could play there. And Peter had buried some treasure in a little plastic bag near the favorite place. But before the children could dig the treasure up again, someone moved into the house. They were sure they wouldn't like the lady, and they went to see Mr. Pell about her.

Mr. PELL'S BAKERY was a block to the south and a little way around the corner. The children didn't even have to cross the street to get there. When they came in at its open doorway Mr. Pell said, "Hello there." He was behind the counter in his white apron, and he seemed to know right away why they had come to see him.

"Well now," he said, "how do you like your new neighbor?"

"I don't like her," Peter said.

"I don't, either," said Suzie.

And Mark just said, "No."

"No?" cried Mr. Pell, and threw up his hands. "I'm surprised at you."

Peter asked, "When will she leave? Did she just rent the place for a while?"

Mr. Pell shrugged his shoulders. "How long she'll live in the house I don't know. But I expect she'll stay a while. She bought it."

"Oh," said Peter, very much disappointed. "She bought it. I guess she'll stay forever then."

The other two were silent. All three looked so sad that Mr. Pell began to feel sorry, too.

"I'm sorry I had to sell it," he said. "I know you like to play there."

He opened his glass case and took out three cookies, scalloped at the edges and sprinkled with sugar. He laid them on the counter.

"Here," he said, pushing them toward the children. "I wish I could have made a present of the place to you — especially the garden house." He bent over the counter, looking at them thoughtfully. "The lady's name is Mrs. Bradley," he offered in a low voice after a while. "I hope you get to like her."

Suzie, Mark, and Peter took the cookies and thanked Mr. Pell. They stood sadly about for a little while longer. Then they went out, eating the cookies. The sugary taste soothed their feelings a little, but not much.

As they walked along Mark said, "That lady's our enemy."

The word struck Suzie and Peter just right.

"Our enemy. Our enemy," they chanted. "That's what she is." It was like letting off steam. And it did help.

Coming toward them they saw Monica and Jean and a boy who lived away off on another block. They had heard what Suzie, Peter, and Mark were shouting. As they came up to them, Jean said, "What's this about an enemy?"

The younger children explained.

Then Peter said once more, "That new lady doesn't like dogs."

And Suzie said, "She yelled at us, so we ran away from the garden house fast."

Mark said, "She has a terrible voice."

Monica exclaimed sympathetically, "It's awful. We better warn everybody. If only a nice lady had moved in there . . ." And she and her friends went on their way.

Peter, Mark, and Suzie soon reached Peter's house. Suzie and Mark stopped and got their things. Then, groaning once more about the lost treasure, they went home. They didn't feel like playing any more.

Peter stayed outdoors by himself. He was pretending to play. But mostly he was looking for a chance to go over to dig up his treasure from the flower bed next door. He could see through the uncurtained kitchen windows that Mrs. Bradley was unpacking things and putting them away in the closets. And the kitchen windows overlooked the flower bed. It seemed she would never get out of that room. Peter grew impatient.

Then he heard barking. It certainly wasn't Jamie, for Peter had left him inside his house. Anyway, it didn't sound like Jamie, or like any of the other dogs of the neighborhood. The barking seemed to come from Mrs. Bradley's screened back porch.

But what would a dog be doing

in the house of a dog-hater like Mrs. Bradley?

Peter tiptoed across the border-line of the lawns till he was close enough to be able to take a good look. There on the porch — why he couldn't believe his eyes, but there was a little dachshund. He could hear Mrs. Bradley talking to it in a gentle voice.

"Come on, Freddie," she was saying. "You might as well give up that barking, pet. You're going to live here, and you'll get used to it in time."

So this lady had a dog of her own and was nice to it! This was very strange.

Peter slipped on around to the street and ran to tell Suzie and Mark. They were as surprised as he was, and came right back with him to see what else went on at Mrs. Bradley's.

Sitting in the grass on Peter's

lawn they kept their eyes glued on the house, and especially on the kitchen. They kept their ears open too.

The little dog had stopped barking and had gone inside, so Suzie and Mark couldn't see it.

"But she didn't like dogs a while ago," Suzie said.

The screen door opened then, and the lady herself came out. The little dog trotted along beside her.

"There he is. There he is." Mark and Peter said it at the same time.

"Oh," Suzie cried, "isn't he darling!"

Mrs. Bradley was a well-filled-out woman of about fifty. She glanced toward the children and said "Hello," in that strange harsh voice.

"Hello," they all answered, but without much enthusiasm. They had to answer her, even though she was their enemy.

While the little dog ran around sniffing at everything, Mrs. Bradley stood looking about her. Then she knelt by the flower bed and let the soft rich earth run through her fingers. She had a piece of paper in her hand, and seemed to sprinkle something from it on the soil.

"What's she doing that for?" Mark asked, without expecting an answer.

Peter groaned. "I wish she'd go away from there," he murmured.

"That's exactly where I buried my treasure."

"It is?" asked Suzie. "You hid it right there?"

And Mark said, "We have to get it back quick, Peter."

They watched the lady closely. If only she wouldn't start digging and find it.

Then to their relief Mrs. Bradley got up. She dusted the earth from her fingers, and said to her dog, "Come, Freddie, let's go and see what else we have in our yard."

She went down the path to the garden house and sat on one of the seats in the shade of the trumpet vine. The little dog chased around. In and out of the garden house he went, all over the lawn, and then he went running back to her.

"I wonder if that little dog and Peter's Jamie will ever get along after they meet," Suzie said after a while. She hoped the little dog wouldn't be afraid of big Jamie.

They all agreed that Freddie was a very nice dog, and that they would like to play with him. But they probably never would since he belonged to that terrible lady.

"She's our enemy," Mark said once more.

Suzie said, "She doesn't look very terrible."

Peter just kept watching. He had even forgotten about his treasure for the moment, he was so busy wondering about the lady.

"But she has a croaky, terrible voice," Mark said. He hoped to go on with this game. It was exciting. He was sorry, in a way, that the lady was so mild-looking.

Peter too was thinking that she was much too rosy-faced and plump and gentle to be a very big enemy. Still, he didn't know much about her yet. He'd go slow about making friends with her.

A big drop of rain fell on his nose. More came splattering down, and then came a quick hard summer shower. The children jumped up squealing, and ran into Peter's house.

Mrs. Cullen, Peter's mother,

gave them a towel and let them dry themselves off. It was several minutes before they thought of looking out of the window to see what had become of their neighbor. There was no one to be seen on the grounds. The lady and her dog must have gone indoors too.

It rained most of the rest of that day and part of the next. Peter couldn't go out and dig for his treasure.

In the middle of the second day the skies began to clear. Peter let Jamie out for a long run, and went out himself too.

He meant to go to Suzie's and Mark's. But just as he came out the front door, he saw Mrs. Bradley leaving her house with Freddie on his leash. He thought with joy that she must be going shopping. Now he'd have the place all to himself and could dig up his treasure.

He'd get it out and bury it on his own grounds, and Suzie and Mark could hunt it here. But then again, he thought, running around to the back, "Maybe I'll keep my nickel now." He could use it.

Coming to the back flower bed of the little brown house next door, he saw that the rain had leveled out the soft earth. There was no sign left of where he had buried the plastic bag. And he had no idea where to begin. But he took a guess and quickly started digging.

It was soon clear that this was the wrong place. So he made another hole next to it. No sign of the plastic bag there, either. He heaved out another big handful of earth. Then the sound of footsteps close by startled him.

He looked up and saw that Mrs. Bradley had returned. She stood almost over him. She seemed awfully big there, and her face looked angry to Peter.

"Son!" she exclaimed in her rasping voice. "Stop that. I just planted that bed with petunia seeds."

Peter got up. "Oh," he said. He was a little scared, and he was sorry.

"Why are you digging here?" she asked, and peered at the two big holes he had made.

The dog, Freddie, went over and sniffed the turned-up earth. He started to scratch there. The lady called him off.

Peter turned and ran. He hadn't meant to hurt her petunias. But how could he explain without telling her the truth? And he didn't want to tell her his secret.

"Wait," the lady called.

But Peter ran on.

Conclusion:

Mrs. Bradley turned out to be a fine neighbor after all. Suzie and Peter and Mark were very sorry they had ever called her "the enemy." In the book *The Favorite Place*, by Irmengarde Eberle, published by Franklin Watts, Inc., Mrs. Bradley adds seven more animals and two more children to the gang that plays in the favorite place.

RED MITTENS

Laura Bannon

Have you ever lost something you loved very much? Then you will sympathize with Little Joe.

"HOLD STILL," said little Joe's Mommie. She slipped some red yarn over his hands and began winding the end into a little ball. The ball grew bigger and bigger until all the yarn was wound onto it. Then Mommie began to knit with four needles.

the meadow stayed in their homes down under the ground to keep warm. But little Joe went out with his sled and made long lovely curves in the smooth snow frosting. His red mittens helped him stay warm as toast.

Little Joe liked his mittens so much he wore them all the time. When summer came, it was too warm to keep them on his hands. So he wound the string around his neck and wore them on the front of his overalls for carrying things.

The cows were let out of the barn to eat the green grass. Small animals scampered about again in the warm sunshine. They were all little Joe's friends and he had long talks with them when he played in the meadow.

"What are you making?" asked little Joe.

"It is a secret. You have to guess," answered Mommie. She smiled as she knit and knit and knit.

"Red mittens!" cried little Joe.

"Yes, a pair of red mittens for you," said Mommie.

When they were finished, she put some fancy black stitches on the back. Then she fastened them together with a long black crocheted string, so he wouldn't lose them.

Little Joe thought they were beautiful.

When the whirling snow came, it piled up in the meadow back of little Joe's house. Every hill looked like a big cake with white frosting.

The small animals that lived in

One day little Joe suddenly stopped playing. His mittens! Where were they?

They were not on the front of his overalls.

They were not in his pockets.

They were not anywhere on the ground.

They were lost. Poor little Joe!

Little Joe couldn't be happy without his mittens. He wandered about looking for them.

A kind hen was scratching for worms among the milkweeds.

"I have lost my beautiful red mittens," little Joe told her.

"Where did you lose them?" asked the hen.

"Somewhere in the meadow," said little Joe. He wanted to cry.

"Don't be sad," said the kind hen. "I have very sharp eyes. I will help you find them."

And so the hen and little Joe looked for the mittens.

They were not around the prickly thistle bushes.

They were not under the big toadstools.

They were not among the tall cat-tails in the marsh where little Joe had been trying to catch frogs.

The red mittens were gone! Little Joe had big tears in his eyes.

"What are you looking for?" asked a friendly pussy-cat who was hunting for field mice in the tall ferns.

"Little Joe has lost his mittens," said the hen.

"My beautiful red mittens!" added little Joe. "We have looked all over the ground for them."

"You just looked on the ground!" exclaimed the friendly cat. "You

should look *high* and *low* for them. I have eyes that can see even in the dark. I will help you find them."

The cat and the hen and little Joe looked *high* and *low*.

Little Joe looked *high*.

They were not on top of the tall bushes.

They were not in the trees.

The hen and the cat looked *low*.

They were not under the big leaves.

They were not in the patch of dandelions.

Poor little Joe began to cry.

By an old stump in the meadow they met a wide-awake cow.

"Did you lose something?" asked the cow.

Little Joe nodded his head. He had a lump in his throat.

"He lost his red mittens," said the hen.

"And we have looked *high* and *low* for them," said the cat.

"You just looked *high* and *low* for them!" exclaimed the wide-awake cow. "You should look *high* and *low* and in the *middle*. I have such big eyes for looking. I will help you find them."

The hen, the cat, the cow and little Joe looked for the mittens.

Little Joe looked *high*.

The cat and the hen looked *low*.

And the cow looked in the *middle*.

They looked everywhere in the meadow.

The mittens were not in the robin's nest in the oak.

They were not in the rabbit's hole at its roots.

They were not in the old shoe the cat found in the tall grass.

Suddenly the cow started to laugh.

She giggled and laughed and laughed and giggled.

Little Joe was surprised.

So were the hen and the cat.

"When a beautiful pair of red mittens is lost, it is not something to laugh about," said the kind hen.

"And it is not good manners," said little Joe.

"But I have found the mittens," cried the wide-awake cow. "Ha! Ha! Ha! You will never guess where."

"They are not *high*," said little Joe.

"They are not *low*," said the cat.

"Where are they?" asked the hen.

"They are in the *middle*," said the cow.

"Show us the mittens," cried little Joe.

"I will show you the mittens if you do as I say," said the cow.

"You stand beside me," the cow said to the hen. The hen did.

"You stand on the other side of me," she said to the cat. The cat did.

"Now you stand in front of me," the cow said to little Joe. Little Joe stood facing the cow.

"Now turn around," said the cow.

Little Joe turned around.

The hen and the cat and the cow laughed and laughed.

Little Joe did not laugh.

"I don't see my mittens," he said.

"Your mittens are in the middle of your back," the hen told him.

"Feel the string around your

neck," said the friendly cat.

Little Joe felt the string around his neck. He pulled the beautiful red mittens to the front where he could see them. How surprised he was to find they had been on his back all the time!

Little Joe was happy again. After that, whenever he met the kind hen or the friendly cat or the wide-awake cow in the meadow, they all had a good laugh about the time he lost his mittens.

Conclusion:

There are many pictures about Little Joe and his red mittens in the book *Red Mittens*, by Laura Bannon, published by Houghton Mifflin Company. Laura Bannon has also written and illustrated *The Scary Thing*, published by Houghton Mifflin Company, and *Manuela's Birthday in Old Mexico*, published by Albert Whitman & Company.

JUMPY

Ilo Orleans

Jumpy was
My turtle-pet;
But, Jumpy ran away —
And where he went
A-wandering —
Jumpy did not say.

I have a can
Of turtle food,
Enough to last a year!
Oh, what will Jumpy
Find to eat?
Not very much, I fear.

Jumpy didn't
Say: "Good-bye!"
How could he be so rude?
I have no turtle
Anymore —
But *lots* of turtle food!

THE ACROBAT

Ilo Orleans

The squirrel skips
Across the wire;
His tight-rope walking
I admire.
He is a clever
Acrobat,
To entertain
His friends like that.

THE TOAD
Ilo Orleans

The toad did not
    Appeal to me
Until I learned
    Around the garden

He eats the pests
    That injure plants —
So I, of course,
    Must beg his pardon!

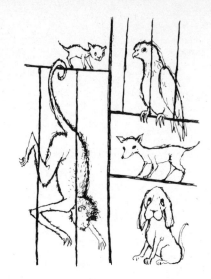

THE ANIMAL STORE
Rachel Field

If I had a hundred dollars to
    spend,
Or maybe a little more,

I'd hurry as fast as my legs would
    go
Straight to the animal store.

I wouldn't say, "How much for
    this or that?" —
"What kind of a dog is he?"
I'd buy as many as rolled an eye,
Or wagged a tail at me!

I'd take the hound with the droop-
    ing ears
That sits by himself alone;
Cockers and Cairns and wobbly
    pups
For to be my very own.

I might buy a parrot all red and
    green,
And the monkey I saw before,
If I had a hundred dollars to
    spend,
Or maybe a little more.

From *Taxis and Toadstools*, by Rachel Field, published by Doubleday & Company, Inc.

AZOR

Maude Crowley

As this story will prove to you, Azor Peach could understand animals. They often told him things that were very useful to know. The grown-ups found all this very hard to believe, but Pringle — the little girl who lived across the street — was very sympathetic.

AZOR PEACH was six years old and he lived in a red house on Elm Street in Marblehead, Massachusetts. He was 47 inches tall, and he weighed 56 pounds, and he had six new teeth. So he was pretty big for his age.

Azor was in the First Grade at the Gerry School. He could read words like SOMETHING and he could spell words like CHICKEN. And he could count up to A TRILLION NINE by skipping a few numbers in between. So he must have been smart, too.

He could ski pretty well, he could swim pretty well, and he could mind his own business *very* well, as you'll see. All in all, there were no flies on Azor.

But there was one strange thing about him. Animals talked to him. They really *did*. It was no "Pussy-horsie-doggie" stuff, either. The things they told him were *important* things.

It wasn't Azor who thought there was anything strange about it. It was other people. Grownups laughed at him and scolded him. Big boys laughed at him and called him a baby. Even quite little boys laughed at him. And of course nobody believed him — except Pringle, and she was only three.

65

One of the animals who told him things was Larry Freeto, the big black-and-white tomcat who lived next door. Larry didn't like anyone much. He didn't like the woman he belonged to, and he didn't like any of the people in town, nor even any of the other animals. He sat on his porch and watched everything with half-closed eyes. Every once in a while he closed his eyes entirely, and sighed.

But he *did* like Azor. He thought Azor had sense. Azor never threw things at him or chased him out of his yard the way the other boys did. And of course Azor never called him "Pussy" or "Kitty" or any other silly name, the way the girls did.

So the morning after Mrs. Woodfin lost the silver earring that had belonged to her grandmother, he jumped down from his porch railing when he saw Azor leaving for school.

"That earring is behind the third right-hand fencepost on Dr. Snow's lawn," he said. "If you want to know."

"Thank you," said Azor.

And after school he walked down to Sapphire Lane and got it, and took it to Mrs. Woodfin's house. She wasn't home, but at suppertime she came to Azor's house and gave him a dollar.

"You're a good boy, Azor," she said, "to go hunting for my earring when you could have been playing with the other boys."

"I didn't go hunting for it," said Azor. "Larry Freeto told me where it was and I just went and got it."

Everybody was in the living

66

room, so they all heard. His mother told him to stop telling stories to Mrs. Woodfin this very minute! His father said he was getting too old for this sort of thing and that it would have to stop. And his big brother Matthew told him not to be a baby *all* his life.

Azor only said, "He really *did*," and went outside.

Conclusion:

Larry Freeto, the cat, was not the only animal to speak to Azor. In the book *Azor,* by Maude Crowley, published by Henry Z. Walck, Inc., Azor also learns things from Mr. Frost's horse and from a turtle and a sea gull.

LITTLE GIRL WITH SEVEN NAMES
Mabel Leigh Hunt

Once there was a little Quaker girl with a name as long as that of any royal princess — Melissa Louisa Amanda Miranda Cynthia Jane Far-low! Seven names, to be exact! Although having so many names was sometimes a nuisance, there was a very special reason for each one, as this story will prove.

It was from Grandmother Melissa Gray that Melissa Louisa got her first name.

Grandmother Gray was one of the dearest grandmothers a little girl ever had. You had to go around the bend of the road, through the covered bridge, past a crossroads, and over two hills before you reached Grandmother Gray's house. So that Melissa Louisa did not see her as often as she would have liked.

But on First Days, when everyone went to Meeting in the little white meeting-house, Grandmother Gray always managed to sit next to Melissa Louisa. She would hold the little girl's hand in her gentle warm one, and Melissa Louisa would lean her head against Grandmother Gray's soft silken shoulder, and sit as quietly as a mouse, even though her feet sometimes went to sleep.

And every First Day, during Meeting, when it was so still that one could have heard a pin drop, the little girl would begin to wonder what surprise lay hidden this time in the pocket of Grandmother Gray's full skirt. Although she tried with all her might not to think about it, and to send little prayers to the Lord, asking Him to help her to be a better girl, it just seemed that she couldn't ever keep from thinking of Grandmother's pocket.

So that by the time Meeting was over, and everyone was shaking hands, and greeting each other, Melissa Louisa was as hungry as a little bear. But she kept it to herself, and never said a word, for she had been taught to be mannerly.

Then Grandmother Gray would fumble among the folds of her silken skirt, until she found her pocket. And out would come a big brown cooky, or a stick of horehound candy, or a peppermint drop. She would hold out the sweet to Melissa Louisa and say, "This will stay thy hunger until thee gets thy dinner, Melissa."

She never bothered about any of the child's other names. The one name of *Melissa* was quite enough for Grandmother Melissa Gray.

Melissa Louisa got her second name from Grandmother Louisa Farlow.

She was a dear grandmother, too, but very different from Grandmother Gray. Her farm adjoined Melissa Louisa's father's farm, so that she lived only a short distance down the road, and Melissa Louisa saw her often. Grandmother Farlow thought that everyone should be good ALL of the time! And no matter how often she saw Melissa Louisa, she would say, "And has thee been a good girl, Louisa-child?"

Grandmother Louisa Farlow never called Melissa Louisa by any other name than *Louisa*.

Aunt Amanda and Aunt Miranda were twins. They lived with Grandmother Gray, for they were her daughters. Melissa Louisa loved them very much. They were slim and pretty, and cared a great deal how they looked when they went to Meeting, or to make calls.

Grandmother Farlow said that "it would be more seemly if Amanda and Miranda Gray spent less time stitching tucks into their petticoats, and more time preparing their souls for the hereafter."

But Melissa Louisa could not help feeling proud of her twin aunts when she saw how very

sweet they looked in their dainty sprigged delaines or calicoes, and she thought that their curls peeped out from under their plain little bonnets in the prettiest way imaginable.

It was impossible to tell them apart, for they were as like as two sweet-pea blossoms. So that when Melissa Louisa saw Aunt Amanda, she would say, "Good day to thee, Aunt Amanda-Miranda."

And when she saw Aunt Miranda she would say, "Good day to thee, Aunt Amanda-Miranda."

For that was perfectly safe, as one of them was bound to be either Aunt Amanda or Aunt Miranda.

The dimples would dance in the pink cheeks of the twin aunts, and

they would say, "Good day to *thee*, little Amanda Miranda."

It was nice to be named for two such charming aunts. Melissa Louisa wished that she had inherited their curls as well as their names.

Aunt Cynthia and Aunt Jane were Father's sisters, and they lived with Grandmother Farlow in the farmhouse just down the road.

Aunt Cynthia was tall and thin. She was very, very good. She was very, very serious. And she spent a great deal of time teaching Melissa Louisa how to sew, how to be mannerly and, above all, how to be GOOD.

For she said, "First thee must please the Lord. But I want my little namesake to be a credit to me, too."

Aunt Jane was short and stout, and very sensible. She liked to milk, and take care of the chickens and the baby animals on the farm. She could make the best butter and cheese of any woman in the countryside. She was also what people called "a natural-born nurse," so that she was away from home a great deal of the time, taking care of sick people.

Aunt Jane said, "Between thee and me, child, the name of *Jane* would have been quite enough for thee. It would have suited thee, too. There aren't any fol-de-rols about *Jane*."

Melissa Louisa often wondered if she could ever be as good as Aunt Cynthia. Or as useful as Aunt Jane. She thought it a great honor to be named for them. But sometimes she felt a little worried for fear she would not grow up to be a credit to them.

All of which explains how Melissa Louisa Amanda Miranda Cynthia Jane Farlow happened to have so many names. Seven names she had — and she thought it was very nice until her first day at school.

Conclusion:

Little Girl With Seven Names was written by Mabel Leigh Hunt and published by J. B. Lippincott Company. Another story in this book tells about the time Melissa Louisa Amanda Miranda Cynthia Jane Farlow minded the babies.

THE TWO LITTLE CATS

Elizabeth Coatsworth

Where are the cats
In all this rain
That bows down the trees
And spouts from the drain,
That blackens the house,
And drums on the roof?
Are the two little cats
In a place rain-proof?

Are the two black cats
All safe and sound

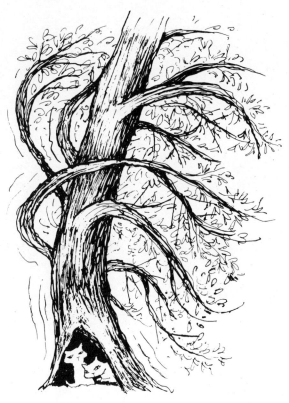

In a cedar cave
With low branches around?
Or are they licking
Their paws fresh white
In the shed whose door
Never yet shut tight?

In the dark of the barn
Would you see four eyes
Gleaming fitful and green
Like fireflies?
We shall never know
But when the rain passes
They'll appear stepping high
Across wet grasses.

From *Country Poems*, by Elizabeth Coatsworth, published by The Macmillan Company.

DANDELIONS

Frances Frost

Over the climbing meadows
Where swallow-shadows float,
These are the small gold buttons
On earth's green, windy coat.

From *Pool in the Meadow*, by Frances Frost, published by Houghton Mifflin Company.

EARLY

Dorothy Aldis

I was up so tip toe early
That the flowers were all pearly
As they waited in their places
For the sun to dry their faces.

From *Everything and Anything*, by Dorothy Aldis, published by G. P. Putnam's Sons.

THE STORM

Dorothy Aldis

In my bed all safe and warm
I like to listen to the storm.
The thunder rumbles loud and
  grand —
The rain goes splash and whisper;
  and
The lightning is so sharp and
  bright
It sticks its fingers through the
  night.

From *Everything and Anything*, by Dorothy Aldis, published by G. P. Putnam's Sons.

72

SKIPPING ROPES

Dorothy Aldis

Someday
Jane shall
Have, she
Hopes,
Rainbows
For her
Skipping
Ropes.

From *Everything and Anything*, by Dorothy Aldis,
published by G. P. Putnam's Sons.

THE POPPY SEED CAKES

Margery Clark

*Come meet Andrewshek and his Auntie Katushka and find out what
happened to the delicious little cakes seasoned with poppy seeds.
Poppy seeds? Where did Auntie Katushka get the poppy seeds she
used in her famous cakes? Why, they came from the old country, of
course. So did her bright shawl and her silk apron. For that matter,
so did Andrewshek's fine feather bed.*

ONCE UPON A TIME there was
a little boy and his name was
Andrewshek. His mother and his
father brought him from the old
country when he was a tiny baby.

Andrewshek had an Auntie Katushka and she came from the old
country, too, on Andrewshek's
fourth birthday.

Andrewshek's Auntie Katushka
came on a large boat. She brought
with her a huge bag filled with
presents for Andrewshek and his
father and his mother. In the huge
bag were a fine feather bed and a
bright shawl and five pounds of
poppy seeds.

The fine feather bed was made
from the feathers of her old green
goose at home. It was to keep Andrewshek warm when he took a
nap.

73

The bright shawl was for Andrewshek's Auntie Katushka to wear when she went to market.

The five pounds of poppy seeds were to sprinkle on little cakes which Andrewshek's Auntie Katushka made every Saturday for Andrewshek.

One lovely Saturday morning Andrewshek's Auntie Katushka took some butter and some sugar and some flour and some milk and seven eggs and she rolled out some nice little cakes. Then she sprinkled each cake with some of the poppy seeds which she had brought from the old country.

While the nice little cakes were baking, she spread out the fine feather bed on top of the big bed, for Andrewshek to take his nap.

Andrewshek did not like to take a nap.

Andrewshek loved to bounce up and down and up and down on his fine feather bed.

Andrewshek's Auntie Katushka took the nice little cakes out of the oven and put them on the table to cool; then she put on her bright shawl to go to market. "Andrewshek," she said, "please watch these cakes while you rest on your fine feather bed. Be sure that the kitten and the dog do not go near them."

"Yes, indeed! I will watch the nice little cakes," said Andrewshek. "And I will be sure that the kitten and the dog do not touch them." But all Andrewshek really did was to bounce up and down and up and down on the fine feather bed.

"Andrewshek!" said Andrewshek's Auntie Katushka. "How can you watch the poppy seed cakes

74

and was scolding as fast as he could. He was wagging his head and was opening and closing his long red beak.

"What do you want?" said Andrewshek. "What are you scolding about?"

"I want all the goose feathers from your fine feather bed," quacked the big green goose. "They are mine."

"They are not yours," said Andrewshek. "My Auntie Katushka brought them with her from the old country in a huge bag."

"They are mine," quacked the big green goose. He waddled over to the fine feather bed and tugged at it with his long red beak.

"Stop, Green Goose," said Andrewshek, "and I will give you one of Auntie Katushka's poppy seed cakes."

"A poppy seed cake!" the green goose quacked in delight. "I love nice little poppy seed cakes! Give me one and you shall have your feather bed."

when all you do is to bounce up and down and up and down on the fine feather bed?" Then Andrewshek's Auntie Katushka, in her bright shawl, hurried off to market.

But Andrewshek kept bouncing up and down and up and down on the fine feather bed and paid no attention to the little cakes sprinkled with poppy seeds.

Just as Andrewshek was bouncing up in the air for the ninth time, he heard a queer noise that sounded like "Hs-s-s-s-sss," at the front door of his house.

"Oh, what a queer noise!" cried Andrewshek. He jumped down off the fine feather bed and opened the front door. There stood a great green goose as big as Andrewshek himself. The goose was very cross

But one poppy seed cake could not satisfy the greedy green goose.

"Give me another!" Andrewshek gave the green goose another poppy seed cake.

"Give me another!" the big green goose hissed and frightened Andrewshek nearly out of his wits.

Andrewshek gave him another and another and another till all the poppy seed cakes were gone.

Just as the last poppy seed cake disappeared down the long neck of the green goose, Andrewshek's Auntie Katushka appeared at the door, in her bright shawl. "Boo! hoo!" cried Andrewshek. "See! That naughty green goose has eaten all the poppy seed cakes."

"What? All my nice little poppy seed cakes?" cried Andrewshek's Auntie Katushka. "The naughty goose!"

The greedy goose tugged at the fine feather bed again with his long red beak and started to drag it to the door. Andrewshek's Auntie Katushka ran after the green goose and just then there was a dreadful explosion. The greedy goose who had stuffed himself with poppy seed cakes had burst and his feathers flew all over the room.

"Well! Well!" said Andrewshek's Auntie Katushka, as she gathered up the pieces of the big green goose. "We soon shall have two fine feather pillows for your fine feather bed."

Conclusion:

Andrewshek has a little friend named Erminka who likes to wear red-topped boots that came from the old country. In the book *The Poppy Seed Cakes*, by Margery Clark, published by Doubleday & Company, Inc., Andrewshek and Erminka have a wonderful tea party and many other good times.

IF YOU MEET A FAIRY

Rose Fyleman

If you meet a fairy
Don't run away;
She won't want to hurt you,
She'll only want to play.

Show her round the garden,
Round the house too,
She'll want to see the kitchen
(I know they always do).

Find a tiny present
To give her when she goes,
They love silver paper
And little ribbon bows.

I knew a little girl once
Who saw twenty-three
Playing in the orchard
As jolly as could be.

They asked her to dance with
   them
To make a twenty-four;
She ran to the nursery
And hid behind the door.

Hid behind the nursery door —
(What a thing to do!)
She grew up very solemn
And rather ugly too.

If you meet a fairy
Remember what I say,
Talk to her nicely
And don't run away.

From *The Fairy Flute*, by Rose Fyleman, published
by Doubleday & Company, Inc.

DIVIDING

David McCord

Here is an apple, ripe and red
On one side; on the other green.
And I must cut it with a knife
Across or in between.

And if I cut it in between,
And give the best (as Mother said)
To you, then I must keep the
   green,

And you will have the red.

But Mother says that green is
   tough
Unless it comes in applesauce.
You *know* what? I've been sick
   enough:
I'll cut it straight across.

From *Far and Few*, by David McCord, published by
Little, Brown & Co.

I AM

Ilo Orleans

I am
A baker
I can bake a cake.

I am
A gardener
I can dig and rake.

I am
A butcher
I have meat to sell.

I am
A doctor
I can make you well.

I am
A tailor
I can sew a coat.

I am
A captain
I can sail a boat.

I am
A barber
I can trim your hair.

I am
A carpenter
I can mend a chair.

I am
A cobbler
I can fix a shoe.

I am
A poet
I make rhymes for you.

SECRET POCKET

Ilo Orleans

I have a very
Secret pocket.
And that is where I hide
So many things —
It's wonderful
They all can get inside.

A whistle, pencil,
Sticks of gum,
A skate key, rubber rings;
Some bottle caps,
A sheriff's badge,
And pebbles, crayons, strings!

My pocket must
Be *very secret*.
If mother learns what's in it,
Instead of being
Full, it would
Be *empty* in a minute!

I WISH I HAD

Ilo Orleans

I haven't got a puppy-dog;
I wish I had a puppy-dog;
So I pretend my puppy-dog
Is trotting after me!

I haven't got a sailing-ship;
I wish I had a sailing-ship;
So I pretend my sailing-ship
    Is sailing on the sea!

I haven't got an aeroplane;
I wish I had an aeroplane;
So I pretend my aeroplane
    Is flying in the sky!

I haven't got a pony-cart;
I wish I had a pony-cart;
So I pretend my pony-cart
    Will be here by-and-by!

PLAYING PAPER DOLLS

Maud Hart Lovelace

Betsy's mother hoped that whoever moved into the house across the street would have a little girl Betsy's age. That was what Betsy hoped too, for though there were plenty of children for her eight-year-old sister Julia, there were no playmates for her. The little girl who moved in was just Betsy's age, and her name was Tacy — short for Anna Anastacia. Betsy and Tacy lived in Minnesota about the time grandmother was a little girl. They had many wonderful times together.

QUITE OFTEN, after school, Betsy and Tacy went to Betsy's house and played paper dolls.

Betsy and Tacy liked paper dolls better than real dolls. They wanted real dolls too, of course. The most important thing to see on Christmas morning, poking out of a stocking or sitting under a tree, was a big china doll . . . with yellow curls and a blue silk dress and bonnet; or with black curls and a pink silk dress and bonnet . . . it didn't matter which. But after Christmas they put those dolls away and played with their paper dolls.

They cut the paper dolls from fashion magazines. They could hardly wait for their mothers' magazines to grow old. Mrs. Benson didn't have any children, so she saved her fashion magazines for Betsy and Tacy. And when Miss Meade, the sewing woman, came to Betsy's house, she could be depended upon to leave a magazine or two behind.

The chief trouble Betsy and Tacy had was in finding pictures of men and boys. There had to be father dolls and brother dolls, of course. The tailor shops had men's fashion sheets. But those fashion sheets were hard to get. Tacy's brother George worked next door to a tailor shop. He told Mr. Baumgarten, the tailor, that his little sister Tacy liked those fash-

ion sheets. After that Mr. Baumgarten saved all his fashion sheets for Tacy, and Tacy divided them with Betsy.

The dolls were not only cut from magazines, they lived in magazines. Betsy and Tacy each had a doll family living in a magazine. The servant dolls were kept in a pile between the first two pages; a few pages on was the pile of father dolls; then came the mother dolls, and then the sixteen-year-olds, the ten-year-olds, the eight-year-olds, the five-year-olds and the babies.

Those were the dolls that Betsy and Tacy played with after school.

Betsy and Tacy stopped in at Tacy's house to get her magazine and eat a cookie. Then they went on to Betsy's house, and when Betsy had kissed her mother and both of them had hung their wraps in the little closet off the back par-

lor, Betsy brought out the magazine in which her doll family lived.

"Shall we play here beside the stove, mamma?" she asked.

"Yes, that would be a good place to play," said Mrs. Ray; and it was.

The fire glowed red through the isinglass windows of the big hard coal heater. It shone on the wild horses' heads which ran in a procession around the shining nickel trim. Up on the warming ledge the tea kettle was singing. Underneath the stove, on the square metal plate which protected the green flowered carpet, Lady Jane Grey, the cat, was singing too.

She opened one sleepy eye but she kept on purring as Betsy and Tacy opened their magazines.

"What shall we name the five-year-old today?" Tacy asked Betsy.

The five-year-olds were the most important members of the large doll families. Everything pleasant happened to them. They had all the adventures.

The eight-year-olds lived very dull lives; and they were always given very plain names. They were Jane and Martha, usually, or Hannah and Jemima. Sometimes Betsy and Tacy forgot and called them Julia and Katie. But the five-year-olds had beautiful names. They were Lucille and Evelyn, or Madeline and Millicent.

"We'll be Madeline and Millicent today," Betsy decided.

They played that it was morning. The servant dolls got up first. The servant dolls wore caps with long streamers and dainty ruffled aprons. They didn't look at all like the hired girls of Hill Street. But like hired girls they got up bright and early.

The fathers and mothers got up next. Then came the children, beginning with the oldest. The five-year-olds came dancing down to breakfast in the fingers of Betsy and Tacy.

"What are you planning to do today, Madeline?" Betsy's father doll asked his five-year-old.

"I'm going to play with Millicent, papá." (Madeline and Millicent pronounced papa, papá.)

"And I'm going to play with Jemima," said Betsy's eight-year-old who was named Hannah today.

"No, Hannah!" said her father.

"You must stay at home and wash the dishes. But Madeline may go. Wouldn't you like to take the carriage, Madeline? You and Millicent could go for a nice ride. Here is a dollar in case you want some candy."

"Oh, thank you, papá," said Madeline. She gave him an airy kiss.

Meanwhile Tacy's dolls were talking in much the same way. Both father dolls were sent quickly down to work; the mothers went shopping; the babies were taken out in their carriages by the pretty servant dolls; and the older children were shut in the magazines. Then Betsy and Tacy each took her five-year-old in hand, and the fun of the game began.

First they went to the candy store under the patent rocker. Madeline's dollar bought an enormous quantity of gum drops and candy corn. Next they sat down in their carriage which was made of a shoebox. There were two strings attached, and Betsy and Tacy were the horses. Madeline and Millicent took a beautiful ride.

They climbed the back parlor sofa; that was a mountain.

"Let's have a picnic," said Madeline. So they did. They picnicked on top of a pillow which had the head of a girl embroidered on it.

They swished through the dangling bamboo curtains which separated the back parlor from the front parlor. And in the front parlor they left their carriage again. They climbed the piano stool; that was a merry-go-round, and of course they had a ride.

After calling on Mrs. Vanderbilt, who lived behind the starched lace curtains at the front parlor window, and Mrs. Astor, who lived under an easel which was draped in purple silk, they slipped by way of the dining room into the back parlor again.

And here they met with their greatest adventure!

The Betsy horse began to rear and snort.

"What's the matter?" asked the Tacy horse.

"A tiger! A tiger!" cried the Betsy horse. She jumped and kicked.

The Tacy horse began to jump and kick too, looking about her for the tiger. Lady Jane Grey was awake and washing her face.

"She's getting ready to eat us!" cried the Betsy horse, leaping.

"Help!" cried the Tacy horse, leaping too.

They leaped so high that they overturned the carriage. Out went Madeline and Millicent on the highway of the green flowered carpet.

"We're running away!" shouted the Betsy horse.

"Whoa! Whoa!" shouted the Tacy horse.

They ran through the rattling bamboo curtains into the front parlor. There they stopped being horses and raced back, out of breath, to be Madeline and Millicent again.

Lady Jane Grey loved to play with paper. She entered obligingly into the game.

"He's biting me!" shrieked Madeline.

"He's scratching me!" shrieked Millicent.

The tiger growled and pounced.

Madeline and Millicent were rescued just in time. The father dolls rushed up and seized them

and jumped into the coal scuttle. Lady Jane Grey jumped in too and jumped out looking black instead of gray, and Betsy and Tacy scrambled in the coal scuttle trying to fish out the father dolls before they got too black. There were never enough father dolls, in spite of Mr. Baumgarten.

Julia and Katie came in just then from skating. The opening door brought in a rush of winter cold and dark.

"Well, for goodness' sake!" they cried. *"For goodness' sake!"* They cried it so loud that Betsy's mother came in from the kitchen, where she was getting supper.

"Betsy!" she cried. "Come straight out here and wash! And use soap and a wash cloth and warm water from the kettle! You too, Tacy."

"Yes, ma'am," said Betsy and Tacy.

When they had washed they put their paper dolls back into the magazines. And Katie helped Tacy into her outside wraps and took her by the hand, and they started home.

Right at the door, Tacy turned around to smile at Betsy. "Whoa!" she said, instead of "Good-bye!"

"Giddap!" said Betsy, instead of "Come again!"

"Whoa!" "Giddap!" "Whoa!" "Giddap!" they said over and over.

"Whatever are you two talking about?" said Julia and Katie crossly, which was just what Betsy and Tacy had hoped they would say.

Conclusion:

This story has been taken from *Betsy-Tacy,* by Maud Hart Lovelace, published by Thomas Y. Crowell Company. Other stories in the book tell about Betsy's birthday party and her first day at school.

85

TED AND NINA HAVE A HAPPY RAINY DAY

Marguerite de Angeli

Rain on Saturday! What could be worse? Especially in the springtime, when a lively brother and sister have been waiting patiently to spend a whole glorious day outdoors. But Mother comes to the rescue, as mothers often do, and Saturday turns out to be a happy rainy day instead of a dreary one.

TED AND NINA stood at the window. They couldn't go outdoors.

Tippy sat near them. He was too short to reach the window sill.

A robin sat on the cherry tree out in the garden.

He sang his happy song. He sang Cheer-up! Cheer-up!

There were buds on the cherry tree.

It was spring!

It was Saturday!

There was no school. There was no kindergarten. *But* — it was raining!

It was raining so hard that the water ran in wiggly lines down the windowpane.

"Look, Nina!" said Ted. "It's crying!"

"Oh," said Nina, "I *did* want to go out today."

"I want to go out, too," said Ted.

Tippy barked. He wanted to go out, too.

Then Mother called from the kitchen.

"Ted! Nina! Can you please come here? I need some help."

Ted and Nina went into the kitchen where Mother was making cookies.

"Nina, will you please get the butter and eggs. Ted, you please get the raisins."

Nina went to the white ice-box. She took out the eggs. She took out the butter. She gave them to Mother.

Tippy wiggled under the stove.

Ted ran over to the little white cupboard. He had to climb up on the kitchen stool. The cupboard is too high for Ted to reach.

He found the raisins.

Mother had the sugar. She had taken the spices from the spice box. The spice box is very old. Grandma used to have it. It is painted bright red with a rose on top. The spice box holds a box for cinnamon, a box for mace, a box for nutmeg, and one for cloves.

Nina loves the old spice box. She would like to have it to keep.

Mother said, "Now stay over here on this side out of the way, and you can watch."

Nina and Ted love to watch Mother bake. Sometimes when they are very good, Mother lets them cut out some of the cookies.

"Mother," said Nina, "may I cut out a *little man?*"

"Yes, you may cut out the man, and Ted, you may cut out *the duck.*"

Mother mixed the dough for the cookies.

She put in some butter.

She put in some sugar.

She put in some eggs.

Then Mother was ready for the spices.

When the spices were mixed in, Mother put in a cup of milk.

Then she carefully measured some flour and some baking powder.

When the flour and baking powder were well mixed with the other things, Mother rolled out the dough on the mixing board.

The board is always scrubbed very white.

The rolling pin is always scrubbed very white, too.

When the dough was ready, Mother tied an apron around Nina's neck.

She tied one around Ted's neck, too.

Nina stood on the little bench Daddy had made for the children. Ted stood on the large pickle crock that Mother turned upside down.

The crock used to be Great-Grandma's when she lived in this house.

Ted and Nina felt *very* important.

The children took turns cutting out *the little men* and *the ducks*. Mother cut out the round cookies with the fancy edge.

The oven was hot, so Mother put the cookies on the big flat cookie pan.

Nina put raisins in for eyes and nose and mouth and a row down the front for buttons on the cookie *men*.

Ted put raisin eyes on the little cookie *ducks*.

Then Mother popped them in the oven.

In a few minutes the cookies were baked and Mother said Ted and Nina could taste them. They were so good Ted and Nina ate several.

Conclusion:

Later in the day, Ted and Nina play in the attic and explore the contents of old boxes and trunks. It's all in the book *Ted and Nina Have a Happy Rainy Day*, by Marguerite de Angeli, published by Doubleday & Company, Inc.

PART II

MOUSE

Hilda Conkling

Little mouse in gray velvet,
Have you had a cheese-breakfast?
There are no crumbs on your coat,
Did you use a napkin?
I wonder what you had to eat,
And who dresses you in gray velvet?

From *Silverhorn*, by Hilda Conkling, published by
J. B. Lippincott Company.

BUTTERFLY

Hilda Conkling

Butterfly,
I like the way you wear your wings.
Show me their colors,
For the light is going.
Spread out their edges of gold,
Before the Sandman puts me to sleep
And evening murmurs by.

From *Silverhorn*, by Hilda Conkling, published by
J. B. Lippincott Company.

LITTLE SNAIL

Hilda Conkling

I saw a little snail
Come down the garden walk.
He wagged his head this way . . . that
    way . . .
Like a clown in a circus.
He looked from side to side
As though he were from a different
    country.
I have always said he carries his house on
    his back . . .
Today in the rain
I saw that it was his umbrella!

From *Silverhorn*, by Hilda Conkling, published by
J. B. Lippincott Company.

THE LITTLE WOODEN DOLL

Margery Williams Bianco

*Little girls have always loved doll stories, particularly those about a
long-forgotten doll that lies neglected for years, only to be found and
loved by a lonely child of another generation. This is one of the most
charming of such stories — one that is well on the way to becoming
a classic.*

I

IN THE ATTIC

THE LITTLE WOODEN doll had lived
so long in the attic that no one
even knew she was there. Such a number of things get stored away in an
attic: broken furniture and disused
trunks, tattered books and old preserve
jars that have lost their tops, and china
that doesn't match — all the things that
nobody wants are put up there, and
there they stay, among the mice and
the cobwebs, and are forgotten.

This attic was just like any other, in-
asmuch as no one living in the house
below really knew what was in it. The
little wooden doll lay in a corner, between an old pile of schoolbooks thick
with dust and a broken bird cage, and
she must have lain there a very long
time, indeed, for she was not at all
like the dolls that one may see now-
adays. All about her the spiders spun
their webs, and the little mice scam-

pered to and fro over the attic floor, and there was a pleasant smell of dust and dry rot.

The little wooden doll was seldom lonely, for there was always someone to talk to. The mice in particular were great gossips; they knew all that went on in the house, for they ran everywhere. They knew where the nuts were stored, and how many cakes the cook baked, and why the last lot of preserves went wrong. They knew, too, just where the store-closet key was, that the housewife had been hunting for high and low these past three weeks, for they had seen her put it there. Nothing happened that the mice did not know about; they were natural busybodies, and all their news they brought to the little doll.

The spiders, too, were good company, but they were inclined to be narrow-minded, and dwelt too much on their own affairs. The old, old spider, who had his web just over the doll's head, was a philosopher; he had poked into all the old books that lay on the attic floor, and for that he was considered eccentric. When he chose to talk he could be most interesting, but

for the most part he was silent; he disliked chatter, and would shake with rage when the young spiders annoyed him. There was a rumor that he had been disappointed in love, but no one really knew the rights of it.

On summer days, when the sun shone, a beam of light came through the attic window. Golden dust motes danced in the beam, and it was beautiful to see. Sometimes, then, a bumblebee would blunder in, or a great, spotted butterfly, or sometimes a swallow would perch at the open window, and all these had news to bring of the outside world: of the cornfields and the flowers and the blue sky. And sometimes at night, when the moonlight lay on the attic floor, the mice would give parties, and to these the little wooden doll was always invited. Those were

gay evenings. All the baby mice were allowed to sit up late, the crickets brought their fiddles to play the dance music, and even the old, fat spider up in the corner would stretch his legs and nod and become quite cheerful.

II

"SOME DAY!"

On the whole the little wooden doll had a pleasant life.

Only sometimes, toward dusk, when the mice were busied on their own affairs, when the spiders dozed in their hammocks, and only the little gray moths fluttered to and fro, a feeling of sadness came over her. For dolls are made for children, and deep in every doll's heart there is a longing to be loved by a child. And at times, when the rain beat on the shingles and the smell of wet earth came up through the attic window, something stirred in the little doll's memory. She recalled dimly a time when someone had really loved her, someone who had carried her about and put her to bed at night, and on rainy days like these played house with her on the nursery floor. It was so

long ago that the little wooden doll could not remember very clearly, but she knew that these things had once happened, and she thought that if only some little child would come again to the attic, and play with her, she would be quite happy.

But there were no children in the old house, and however eagerly the little doll listened, no one ever came up the attic stairs.

Still, she never quite lost hope. Sitting there in her corner, while the mice played about her, she would think, "Someday, perhaps, a little girl will come up here and find me, and then how pleased she will be!" And she made up a little story to herself of all the things they would do and the games they would play; playing house would be the nicest of all, for every doll loves playing house. She had forgotten what

92

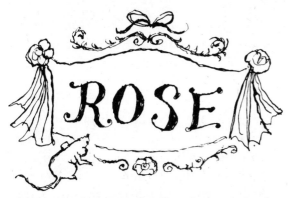

ROSE

who found her might call her Rose, for that seemed to her the loveliest name in the world, and when she told the mice stories, on winter evenings, that was the name she always gave to the heroine.

Conclusion:

The Little Wooden Doll, by Margery Williams Bianco, published by The Macmillan Company, goes on to tell about the children who came to live in the house and about the time the mice held a council to help the little wooden doll.

her own name used to be, it was so long ago, but she hoped that the little girl

CHARLOTTE

E. B. White

Wilbur the pig is very lonely living in the barn, even though he has many neighbors. The goose is too busy sitting on her eggs to bother with Wilbur. The lamb looks down on him, and won't play either. Templeton the rat won't do anything for anybody unless there is something in it for him. Wilbur is sobbing in despair when a small voice asks: "Do you want a friend, Wilbur? I'll be a friend to you." "But I can't see you," exclaims the startled pig. "Go to sleep. You'll see me in the morning," answers the strange voice. And that is how Charlotte came into Wilbur's life.

THE NIGHT seemed long. Wilbur's stomach was empty and his mind was full. And when your stomach is empty and your mind is full, it's always hard to sleep.

A dozen times during the night Wilbur woke and stared into the blackness, listening to the sounds and trying to figure out what time it was. A barn is never perfectly quiet. Even at midnight there is usually something stirring.

The first time he woke, he heard Templeton gnawing a hole in the grain bin. Templeton's teeth scraped loudly against the wood and made quite a racket. "That crazy rat!" thought Wilbur. "Why does he have to stay up all night, grinding his clashers and destroying people's property? Why can't he go to sleep, like any decent animal?"

The second time Wilbur woke, he heard the goose turning on her nest and chuckling to herself.

"What time is it?" whispered Wilbur to the goose.

"Probably-obably-obably about half-past eleven," said the goose. "Why aren't you asleep, Wilbur?"

"Too many things on my mind," said Wilbur.

"Well," said the goose, "that's not *my* trouble. I have nothing at all on my mind, but I've too many things under my behind. Have you ever tried to sleep while sitting on eight eggs?"

"No," replied Wilbur. "I suppose it *is* uncomfortable. How long does it take a goose egg to hatch?"

"Approximately-oximately thirty days, all told," answered the goose.

"But I cheat a little. On warm afternoons, I just pull a little straw over the eggs and go out for a walk."

Wilbur yawned and went back to sleep. In his dreams he heard again the voice saying, "I'll be a friend to you. Go to sleep — you'll see me in the morning."

About half an hour before dawn, Wilbur woke and listened. The barn was still dark. The sheep lay motionless. Even the goose was quiet. Overhead, on the main floor, nothing stirred: the cows were resting, the horses dozed. Templeton had quit work and gone off somewhere on an errand. The only sound was a slight scraping noise from the rooftop, where the weather-vane swung back and forth. Wilbur loved the barn when it was like this — calm and quiet, waiting for light.

"Day is almost here," he thought.

Through a small window, a faint gleam appeared. One by one the stars went out. Wilbur could see the goose a few feet away. She sat with head tucked under a wing. Then he could see the sheep and the lambs. The sky lightened.

94

"Oh, beautiful day, it is here at last! Today I shall find my friend."

Wilbur looked everywhere. He searched his pen thoroughly. He examined the window ledge, stared up at the ceiling. But he saw nothing new. Finally he decided he would have to speak up. He hated to break the lovely stillness of dawn by using his voice, but he couldn't think of any other way to locate the mysterious new friend who was nowhere to be seen. So Wilbur cleared his throat.

"Attention, please!" he said in a loud, firm voice. "Will the party who addressed me at bedtime last night kindly make himself or herself known by giving an appropriate sign or signal!"

Wilbur paused and listened. All the other animals lifted their heads and stared at him. Wilbur blushed. But he was determined to get in touch with his unknown friend.

"Attention, please!" he said. "I will repeat the message. Will the party who addressed me at bedtime last night kindly speak up. Please tell me where you are, if you are my friend!"

The sheep looked at each other in disgust.

"Stop your nonsense, Wilbur!" said the oldest sheep. "If you have a new friend here, you are probably disturbing his rest; and the quickest way to spoil a friendship is to wake somebody up in the morning before he is ready. How can you be sure your friend is an early riser?"

"I beg everyone's pardon," whispered Wilbur. "I didn't mean to be objectionable."

He lay down meekly in the manure, facing the door. He did not know it, but his friend was very near. And the old sheep was right — the friend was still asleep.

Soon Lurvy appeared with slops for breakfast. Wilbur rushed out, ate everything in a hurry, and licked the trough. The sheep moved off down the lane, the gander waddled along behind them, pulling grass. And then, just as Wilbur was settling down for his morning nap, he heard again the thin voice that had addressed him the night before.

"Salutations!" said the voice.

Wilbur jumped to his feet. "Salu-*what*?" he cried.

"Salutations!" repeated the voice.

"What are *they* and where are *you*?" screamed Wilbur. "Please, *please*, tell me where you are. And what are salutations?"

"Salutations are greetings," said the voice. "When I say 'salutations,' it's just my fancy way of saying hello or good morning. Actually, it's a silly expression, and I am surprised that I used it at all. As for my whereabouts, that's easy. Look up here in the corner of the doorway! Here I am. Look, I'm waving!"

At last Wilbur saw the creature that had spoken to him in such a kindly way. Stretched across the upper part of the doorway was a big spiderweb, and

I could see you, Wilbur, as clearly as you can see me."

"Why can't you?" asked the pig. "I'm right here."

"Yes, but I'm near-sighted," replied Charlotte. "I've always been dreadfully near-sighted. It's good in some ways, not so good in others. Watch me wrap up this fly."

A fly that had been crawling along Wilbur's trough had flown up and blundered into the lower part of Charlotte's web and was tangled in the sticky threads. The fly was beating its wings furiously, trying to break loose and free itself.

"First," said Charlotte, "I dive at him." She plunged headfirst toward the fly. As she dropped, a tiny silken thread unwound from her rear end.

"Next, I wrap him up." She grabbed the fly, threw a few jets of silk around it, and rolled it over and over, wrapping it so that it couldn't move. Wilbur watched in horror. He could hardly believe what he was seeing, and although he detested flies, he was sorry for this one.

"There!" said Charlotte. "Now I knock him out, so he'll be more comfortable." She bit the fly. "He can't feel a thing now," she remarked. "He'll make a perfect breakfast for me."

"You mean you *eat* flies?" gasped Wilbur.

"Certainly. Flies, bugs, grasshoppers, choice beetles, moths, butterflies, tasty cockroaches, gnats, midges, daddy longlegs, centipedes, mosquitoes, crickets — anything that is careless enough to get caught in my web. I have to live, don't I?"

hanging from the top of the web, head down, was a large gray spider. She was about the size of a gumdrop. She had eight legs, and she was waving one of them at Wilbur in friendly greeting. "See me now?" she asked.

"Oh, yes indeed," said Wilbur. "Yes indeed! How are you? Good morning! Salutations! Very pleased to meet you. What is your name, please? May I have your name?"

"My name," said the spider, "is Charlotte."

"Charlotte what?" asked Wilbur eagerly.

"Charlotte A. Cavatica. But just call me Charlotte."

"I think you're beautiful," said Wilbur.

"Well, I *am* pretty," replied Charlotte. "There's no denying that. Almost all spiders are rather nice-looking. I'm not as flashy as some, but I'll do. I wish

"Why, yes, of course," said Wilbur. "Do they taste good?"

"Delicious. Of course, I don't really eat them. I drink them — drink their blood. I love blood," said Charlotte, and her pleasant, thin voice grew even thinner and more pleasant.

"Don't say that!" groaned Wilbur. "Please don't say things like that!"

"Why not? It's true, and I have to say what is true. I am not entirely happy about my diet of flies and bugs, but it's the way I'm made. A spider has to pick up a living somehow or other, and I happen to be a trapper. I just naturally build a web and trap flies and other insects. My mother was a trapper before me. Her mother was a trapper before her. All our family have been trappers. Way back for thousands and thousands of years we spiders have been laying for flies and bugs."

"It's a miserable inheritance," said Wilbur, gloomily. He was sad because his new friend was so bloodthirsty.

"Yes, it is," agreed Charlotte. "But I can't help it. I don't know how the first spider in the early days of the world happened to think up this fancy idea of spinning a web, but she did, and it was clever of her, too. And since then, all of us spiders have had to work the same trick. It's not a bad pitch, on the whole."

"It's cruel," replied Wilbur, who did not intend to be argued out of his position.

"Well, *you* can't talk," said Charlotte. "*You* have your meals brought to you in a pail. Nobody feeds me. I have to get my own living. I live by my wits. I have to be sharp and clever, lest I go hungry. I have to think things out, catch what I can, take what comes. And it just so happens, my friend, that what comes is flies and insects and bugs. And *further*more," said Charlotte, shaking one of her legs, "do you realize that if I didn't catch bugs and eat them, bugs would increase and multiply and get so numerous that they'd destroy the earth, wipe out everything?"

"Really?" said Wilbur. "I wouldn't want *that* to happen. Perhaps your web is a good thing after all."

The goose had been listening to this conversation and chuckling to herself. "There are a lot of things Wilbur doesn't know about life," she thought. "He's really a very innocent little pig. He doesn't even know what's going to happen to him around Christmastime; he has no idea that Mr. Zuckerman and Lurvy are plotting to kill him." And the goose raised herself a bit and poked her eggs a little further under her so that they would receive the full heat from her warm body and soft feathers.

97

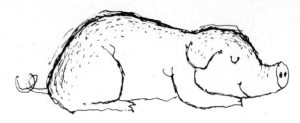

Charlotte stood quietly over the fly, preparing to eat it. Wilbur lay down and closed his eyes. He was tired from his wakeful night and from the excitement of meeting someone for the first time. A breeze brought him the smell of clover — the sweet-smelling world beyond his fence. "Well," he thought, "I've got a new friend, all right. But what a gamble friendship is! Charlotte is fierce, brutal, scheming, bloodthirsty — everything I don't like. How can I learn to like her, even though she is pretty and, of course, clever?"

Wilbur was merely suffering the doubts and fears that often go with finding a new friend. In good time he was to discover that he was mistaken about Charlotte. Underneath her rather bold and cruel exterior, she had a kind heart, and she was to prove loyal and true to the very end.

Conclusion:

In the book *Charlotte's Web*, by E. B. White, published by Harper & Brothers, Wilbur and Charlotte become true friends and have many happy times together. The day comes when Wilbur's life is in danger, and Charlotte has a chance to prove her friendship and devotion.

MY FATHER MEETS SOME TIGERS

Ruth Stiles Gannett

The "my father" of this story was called Elmer Elevator when he was a little boy. Elmer heard from his friend the cat, who had been to Wild Island, about a baby dragon that had been captured by the animals there. Being a kind-hearted boy, Elmer set out to rescue the dragon, but he little dreamed what hair-raising escapes he would have on Wild Island.

THE RIVER was very wide and muddy, and the jungle was very gloomy and dense. The trees grew close to each other, and what room there was between them was taken up by great high ferns with sticky leaves. My father hated to leave the beach, but he decided to start along the river bank where at least the jungle wasn't quite so thick. He ate three tangerines, making sure to keep all the peels this time, and put on his rubber boots.

My father tried to follow the river bank but it was very swampy, and as he went farther the swamp became deeper. When it was almost as deep as

98

river made a very sharp curve away from him just a little way beyond, and so as he walked straight ahead he was getting farther and farther away from the river.

It was very hard to walk in the jungle. The sticky leaves of the ferns caught at my father's hair, and he kept tripping over roots and rotten logs. Sometimes the trees were clumped so closely together that he couldn't squeeze between them and had to walk a long way around.

He began to hear whispery noises, but he couldn't see any animals any-

his boot tops he got stuck in the oozy, mucky mud. My father tugged and tugged, and nearly pulled his boots right off, but at last he managed to wade to a drier place. Here the jungle was so thick that he could hardly see where the river was. He unpacked his compass and figured out the direction he should walk in order to stay near the river. But he didn't know that the

where. The deeper into the jungle he went the surer he was that something was following him, and then he thought he heard whispery noises on both sides of him as well as behind. He tried to run, but he tripped over more roots, and the noises only came nearer. Once or twice he thought he heard something laughing at him.

At last he came out into a clearing and ran right into the middle of it so that he could see anything that might try to attack him. Was he surprised when he looked and saw fourteen green eyes coming out of the jungle all around the clearing, and when the

green eyes turned into seven tigers! The tigers walked around him in a big circle, looking hungrier all the time, and then they sat down and began to talk.

"I suppose you thought we didn't know you were trespassing in our jungle!"

Then the next tiger spoke. "I suppose you're going to say you didn't know it was our jungle!"

"Did you know that not one explorer has ever left this island alive?" said the third tiger.

My father thought of the cat and knew this wasn't true. But of course he had too much sense to say so. One doesn't contradict a hungry tiger.

The tigers went on talking in turn. "You're our first little boy, you know. I'm curious to know if you're especially tender."

"Maybe you think we have regular meal-times, but we don't. We just eat whenever we're feeling hungry," said the fifth tiger.

"And we're very hungry right now. In fact, I can hardly wait," said the sixth.

"I *can't* wait!" said the seventh tiger.

And then all the tigers said together in a loud roar, "Let's begin right now!" and they moved in closer.

My father looked at those seven hungry tigers, and then he had an idea. He quickly opened his knapsack and took out the chewing gum. The cat had told him that tigers were especially fond of chewing gum, which was very scarce on the island. So he threw them each a piece, but they only growled, "As fond as we are of chewing gum, we're sure we'd like you even better!" and they moved so close that he could feel them breathing on his face.

"But this is very special chewing gum," said my father. "If you keep on chewing it long enough it will turn green, and then if you plant it, it will grow more chewing gum, and the sooner you start chewing the sooner you'll have more."

The tigers said, "Why, you don't say! Isn't that fine!" And as each one wanted to be the first to plant the chewing gum, they all unwrapped their pieces and began chewing as hard as they could. Every once in a while one tiger would look into another's mouth and say, "Nope, it's not done yet," until finally they were all so busy looking into each other's mouths to make sure that no one was getting ahead that they forgot all about my father.

Conclusion:

Other chapters in the book *My Father's Dragon,* by Ruth Stiles Gannett, published by Random House, tell how Elmer outwitted lions and wild boars.

TREES

Harry Behn

Trees are the kindest things I know,
They do no harm, they simply grow

And spread a shade for sleepy cows,
And gather birds among their boughs.

They give us fruit in leaves above,
And wood to make our houses of,

And leaves to burn on Hallowe'en,
And in the Spring new buds of green.

They are the first when day's begun
To touch the beams of morning sun,

They are the last to hold the light
When evening changes into night,

And when a moon floats on the sky
They hum a drowsy lullaby

Of sleepy children long ago . . .
Trees are the kindest things I know.

From *The Little Hill* by Harry Behn, published by Harcourt, Brace and Company.

THE SUGAR SNOW

Laura Ingalls Wilder

Almost a hundred years ago, Laura Ingalls and her sister Mary and baby sister Carrie lived with Ma and Pa in a little log house on the edge of the Big Woods of Wisconsin. The family raised all their own food and took very good care of themselves in the midst of the wilderness. Although they worked hard, they also had many good times — and wonderful treats, too, such as maple sugar candy when there was a long run of sap.

FOR DAYS the sun shone and the weather was warm. There was no frost on the windows in the mornings. All day the icicles fell one by one from the eaves with soft smashing and crackling sounds in the snowbanks beneath. The trees shook their wet, black branches, and chunks of snow fell down.

When Mary and Laura pressed their noses against the cold window pane they could see the drip of water from the eaves and the bare branches of the trees. The snow did not glitter; it looked soft and tired. Under the trees it was pitted where the snow was piled like feathers, and it lay in mounds along the top of the rail fence, and stood up in great white balls on top of the gate-posts.

Pa came in, shaking the soft snow from his shoulders and stamping it from his boots.

"It's a sugar snow," he said.

Laura put her tongue quickly to a little bit of the white snow that lay in a fold of his sleeve. It was nothing but wet on her tongue, like any snow. She was glad that nobody had seen her taste it.

"Why is it a sugar snow, Pa?" she asked him, but he said he didn't have time to explain now. He must hurry away, he was going to Grandpa's.

Grandpa lived far away in the Big Woods, where the trees were closer together and larger.

Laura stood at the window and watched Pa, big and swift and strong, walking away over the snow. His gun was on his shoulder, his hatchet and powder horn hung at his side, and his tall boots made great tracks in the soft snow. Laura watched him till he was out of sight in the woods.

It was late before he came home that night. Ma had already lighted the lamp when he came in. Under one arm he carried a large package, and in the other hand was a big, covered, wooden bucket.

"Here, Caroline," he said, handing the package and the bucket to Ma, and then he put the gun on its hooks over the door.

"If I'd met a bear," he said, "I couldn't have shot him without dropping my load." Then he laughed. "And if I'd dropped that bucket and bundle, I wouldn't have had to shoot him. I could have stood and watched him eat what's in them and lick his chops."

Ma unwrapped the package and there were two hard, brown cakes, each

as large as a milk pan. She uncovered the bucket, and it was full of dark brown syrup.

"Here, Laura and Mary," Pa said, and he gave them each a little round package out of his pocket.

They took off the paper wrappings, and each had a little, hard, brown cake, with beautifully crinkled edges.

"Bite it," said Pa, and his blue eyes twinkled.

Each bit off one little crinkle, and it was sweet. It crumbled in their mouths. It was better even than their Christmas candy.

"Maple sugar," said Pa.

Supper was ready, and Laura and Mary laid the little maple sugar cakes beside their plates, while they ate the maple syrup on their bread.

After supper, Pa took them on his knees as he sat before the fire, and told them about his day at Grandpa's, and the sugar snow.

"All winter," Pa said, "Grandpa has been making wooden buckets and little troughs. He made them of cedar and white ash, for those woods won't give a bad taste to the maple syrup.

"To make the troughs, he split out little sticks as long as my hand and as big as my two fingers. Near one end, Grandpa cut the stick half through, and split one half off. This left him a flat stick, with a square piece at one end. Then with a bit he bored a hole lengthwise through the square part, and with his knife he whittled the wood till it was only a thin shell around the round hole. The flat part of the stick he hollowed out with his knife till it was a little trough.

"He made dozens of them, and he made ten new wooden buckets. He had them all ready when the first warm weather came and the sap began to move in the trees.

"Then he went into the maple woods and with the bit he bored a hole in each maple tree, and he hammered the round end of the little trough into the hole, and he set a cedar bucket on the ground under the flat end.

"The sap, you know, is the blood of a tree. It comes up from the roots, when warm weather begins in the spring, and it goes to the very tip of each branch and twig, to make the green leaves grow.

"Well, when the maple sap came to the hole in the tree, it ran out of the tree, down the little trough and into the bucket."

"Oh, didn't it hurt the poor tree?" Laura asked.

"No more than it hurts you when you prick your finger and it bleeds," said Pa.

"Every day Grandpa puts on his boots and his warm coat and his fur cap and he goes out into the snowy woods and gathers the sap. With a barrel on a sled, he drives from tree to tree and empties the sap from the buckets into the barrel. Then he hauls it to a big iron kettle, that hangs by a chain from a cross-timber between two trees.

"He empties the sap into the iron kettle. There is a big bonfire under the kettle, and the sap boils, and Grandpa watches it carefully. The fire must be hot enough to keep the sap boiling, but not hot enough to make it boil over.

"Every few minutes the sap must be skimmed. Grandpa skims it with a big, long-handled, wooden ladle that he made of basswood. When the sap gets too hot, Grandpa lifts ladlefuls of it high in the air and pours it back slowly. This cools the sap a little and keeps it from boiling too fast.

"When the sap has boiled down just enough, he fills the buckets with the syrup. After that, he boils the sap until it grains when he cools it in a saucer.

"The instant the sap is graining, Grandpa jumps to the fire and rakes it all out from beneath the kettle. Then as fast as he can, he ladles the thick syrup into the milk pans that are standing ready. In the pans the syrup turns to cakes of hard, brown maple sugar."

"So that's why it's a sugar snow, because Grandpa is making sugar?" Laura asked.

"No," Pa said. "It's called a sugar snow, because a snow this time of year means that men can make more sugar. You see, this little cold spell and the snow will hold back the leafing of the trees, and that makes a longer run of sap.

104

"When there's a long run of sap, it means that Grandpa can make enough maple sugar to last all the year, for common every day. When he takes his furs to town, he will not need to trade for much store sugar. He will get only a little store sugar, to have on the table when company comes."

"Grandpa must be glad there's a sugar snow," Laura said.

"Yes," Pa said, "he's very glad. He's going to sugar off again next Monday, and he says we must all come."

Pa's blue eyes twinkled; he had been saving the best for the last, and he said to Ma:

"Hey, Caroline! There'll be a dance!"

Ma smiled. She looked very happy, and she laid down her mending for a minute. "Oh, Charles!" she said.

Then she went on with her mending, but she kept on smiling. She said, "I'll wear my delaine."

Ma's delaine dress was beautiful. It was a dark green, with a little pattern all over it that looked like ripe strawberries. A dressmaker had made it, in the East, in the place where Ma came from when she married Pa and moved out west to the Big Woods in Wisconsin. Ma had been very fashionable, before she married Pa, and a dressmaker had made her clothes.

The delaine was kept wrapped in paper and laid away. Laura and Mary had never seen Ma wear it, but she had shown it to them once. She had let them touch the beautiful dark red buttons that buttoned the basque up the front, and she had shown them how neatly the whalebones were put in the seams, inside, with hundreds of little criss-cross stitches.

It showed how important a dance was, if Ma was going to wear the beautiful delaine dress. Laura and Mary were excited. They bounced up and down on Pa's knees, and asked questions about the dance until at last he said:

"Now you girls run along to bed! You'll know all about the dance when you see it. I have to put a new string on my fiddle."

There were sticky fingers and sweet mouths to be washed. Then there were

105

prayers to be said. By the time Laura and Mary were snug in their trundle bed, Pa and the fiddle were both singing, while he kept time with his foot on the floor:

"I'm Captain Jinks of the Horse Marines,
 I feed my horse on corn and beans,
 And I often go beyond my means,
 For I'm Captain Jinks of the Horse Marines,
 I'm captain in the army!"

Conclusion:

In the book *Little House in the Big Woods*, by Laura Ingalls Wilder, published by Harper & Brothers, you can read about Christmas in the Big Woods, the dance at Grandpa's, and other wonderful times in Laura's childhood.

RIDDLE THIS, RIDDLE THAT

Leon Wilson

Cody Capshaw was ten years old before he paid any attention to one of his mother's favorite songs. He knew the tune so well he could almost whistle it backwards, but he couldn't sing it because he'd never paid a nickel's worth of attention to the words. Then one morning, while he was carrying firewood to keep the wash kettle boiling, Cody discovered that the song was a riddle. But no one would tell him the answers — not his mother, Callie, nor his father, Milt, nor his little sister, Omalia. They said he had to unriddle the riddle himself.

HERE IS CALLIE'S SONG. See if it does anything to you, then I'll tell you what it did to Cody.

I gave my love a cher-ry that hath no stone,

I gave my love a chick-en that hath no bone,

I gave my love a thim-ble that hath no end,

I gave my love a ba-by that's a no cry-en

A riddle song!

Now if you have heard someone sing this song and you paid attention to the words, it won't do much to you. But if you don't know these four riddles, maybe you'd better follow along here and see what happened to this boy Cody.

He was paying particular attention to the song this time because it was guiding him to the fire with his load of wood. When he heard the last riddle

106

"You've never listened to my song," Callie said.

"Sure I have!" Cody replied stoutly. "I've heard you sing it hundreds of times." And to show her he wasn't just making this up, he sang the questions that were making his head tickle, like this:

How can there be a cher-ry that hath no stone?

How can there be a chick-en that hath no bone?

How can there be a thim-ble that hath no end?

How can there be a ba-by that's a no cry-en?

— crash! Down went the wood, his mouth fell open in astonishment, and he clapped his hands on his head to stop the tickling that had begun in it.

His mother was a little worried. "You're sick," she said.

Omalia guessed what the trouble was. "Those riddles have got him bothered," she said.

"How can those things be?" Cody asked, his face twisted up with hard thinking. "How can there be a cherry without a stone and how can there be a chicken without bones and how can a thimble not have an end and I sure never yet saw a baby that didn't cry."

"Why, Cody!" his mother exclaimed, "can I believe my ears?" And she began to laugh.

Cody felt his face get warm and begin to prickle and he knew it was turning red. Something, he knew, was wrong or his mother wouldn't be laughing at him. Not this way.

"Well," said Callie, "you know the song sure enough — how come you don't know the riddles?"

Cody could tell from the way his face felt that it was now nearly as red as a tomato. "I reckon you never sang the answers," he said, and he looked at the ground and began stirring it with his toes the way you do when someone asks you something and you come back with an answer you know doesn't amount to much.

Callie laughed again. "I've never once sung that song that I didn't sing the answers too," she said.

"Maybe Cody didn't have his pay-attention earmuffs on," Omalia suggested.

Out of the corner of one eye, Cody could see Omalia grinning at him. "So you know the answers, do you?" he said to himself.

He looked up at his mother again with his best grin on his face. "What

are we waiting for?" he asked. "Sing the answers now."

For a minute Callie didn't say anything. She appeared to be thinking, looking past Cody at the steaming washpot. When she looked back at Cody, she was smiling. "I haven't time right now," she said. "I've got to finish this big wash."

"After the wash is finished, sing them?" Cody begged. For a minute he thought she was going to give in, so he said quickly: "I'll hang the wash on the line for you, I'll empty the tub and put it away. I'll roll the washpot off the fire."

"After I finish here," Callie said, "I have to sweep the house and make the beds."

Cody began to get worried. "After you sweep the house and make the beds?"

"Got to churn the butter then," Callie said. "And after I churn the butter, I have to sew a peck of buttons on your shirts and cook dinner."

"You mean I have to wait *that* long to find out how a chicken can get around without bones?" Cody asked.

"Afraid you do," Callie said, "unless you can think out the answers for your-

self or get Omalia to tell them to you."

"They're easy," Omalia said. "I believe even if I didn't know them I could figure them out."

Cody pretended not to hear Omalia. "You mean I have to wait till dinner," he asked his mother, "to find out how there can be an endless thimble and a cryless babe and a stoneless cherry?"

"I'm mighty afraid so," Callie said firmly. "Hop out of my way now and let me put some of this wood you brought me on my fire."

"Yow!" Cody yelped. "I plan out a wonderful morning and now I have to spend it getting rid of this dratted riddle-tickle!"

Grabbing his head again (for it was tickling worse every minute), Cody hopped out of Callie's way and Omalia's way, and twenty-two hops later he was in the middle of the field back of the house where his father was plowing.

As the plow came along, he ducked between the handles in front of his father and began helping guide the plow as the silver blade ripped up the heavy earth and threw it over. Cody

had a theory that plowing might get the riddles out of his head. He was wrong. He was so busy riddling that he forgot to yell "Haw!" when Luther, the horse, pulled the plow to the end of the row.

"Haw!" Milt yelled, and old Luther swung around to plow another row. "You're mighty quiet today, Cody," Milt said.

"I'm thinking," Cody said, "wondering how can there be a stoneless cherry and a boneless chicken."

"Riddles," said Milt.

"You're mighty whistlin', riddles!" Cody agreed. "Sure wish I could guess 'em — they got me bothered sick."

"Here's a riddle I like a lot," Milt said. "See if you can guess this one:

"I'm alive at both ends
    And dead in the middle.
If you guess this riddle
    I'll give you a fiddle."

Cody thought hard for a minute. And then for another minute. For two min-

utes he really worked. Then he sighed. "That's *five* I can't answer," he said.

"Seems to me you're giving up mighty easy," Milt said. "But I'll tell you. It's us plowing."

"Us plowing?" Cody echoed in amazement. "Great day, what's alive at both ends about us?"

"Luther's alive at one end," Milt said, "and you and I are alive at the other end."

"What's dead in the middle?" Cody demanded.

"The plow," said Milt.

Cody grinned from ear to ear. "Sure enough, you've answered it right," he said. "Now how about answering me the cryless baby one and the endless thimble?"

"Didn't your mother sing you the answers to those riddles?" Milt asked.

"She said she was too busy," Cody told him.

"Then I reckon *I'm* too busy," Milt said. He looked down at Cody and smiled at him. "It won't ruin you to work on them awhile," he said.

"Golly, I hope it won't!" Cody said. With this, he ducked out of the plow and let his father and Luther plow on without him, alive at both ends and dead in the middle.

Twisting a handful of his hair to help himself think, he walked down the road by himself.

At least he *thought* he was by himself.

He hadn't walked far before a red-bird came flying up the road toward him. Quick as a flash he made a wish (you always wish when you see a red-bird flying) — "Wish I was a riddle

109

champion!" — and then he turned to see if the redbird was going to fly up and give him his wish or fly down and make things hard for him.

And smack behind him, close enough to touch, he found someone with pigtails smiling at him.

He frowned fiercely. "Who said *you* could come?"

It was Omalia of course. Cody hadn't heard her following him because her bare feet made no more noise hitting the dusty road than his did, which was none whatsoever.

"I know the answers to those song riddles," she said. "If you let me come with you and you get so beriddled you go crazy, I can tell them to you."

Cody didn't know what to say, so he

said nothing. He had a right to be annoyed with Omalia because she wouldn't tell him the answers right now, but also, maybe it would be wise to have her come along in case he started going cross-eyed from hard thinking.

Omalia could see that Cody was having trouble making up his mind. "Tell you a riddle if you let me come with you," she said. "An easy one — listen:

"It goes up and down a tree.
It has eyes but cannot see."

Cody marched on down the road pretending he hadn't heard the riddle. "Drat the girl," he said to himself. "And drat riddles!"

"Can't you guess it?" Omalia asked.

"You said it was easy," Cody replied. "What the dickens is it?"

"A button," said Omalia.

"Aw, that's a dumb riddle," Cody said. "Who in the world ever saw a button go up and down a tree?"

"They sure climb trees when they're on your shirts!" Omalia said.

Cody knew she was right, but he wished he didn't have to admit it, even to himself. A girl, seven years old, knowing the answers to riddles a ten-year-old boy didn't know — something was mighty wrong!

He was wishing he could think of a riddle to spring on Omalia — a good hard one — when he caught sight of Orvel Swinney. "Look who's out hoeing his corn," he told Omalia, and he began dragging slower and slower in hopes Mr. Swinney would notice him.

He was sure the big man could help him if he would. Anyone who knew as many odd and interesting things as Mr. Swinney did ought to know most every riddle that was ever invented.

"Where you two young ones headed so all-fired fast?" Mr. Swinney inquired.

"Nowhere," Cody replied, "and we got nothing to do when we get there."

"That's a good one!" Mr. Swinney declared, and he threw his big red face back and laughed. "Why don't you hop over the fence and help me chop these weeds out of my corn?" he suggested. "Maybe I can think of something to tell you that you'd like to know."

This, of course, was the very invitation Cody had hoped for. He began to grin. "Help you hoe your corn," he asked, "will you answer a few riddles for me?"

"Riddles?" Mr. Swinney lifted his hat off and began to scratch his shiny bald head. "That's one subject I'm not much of an expert on," he said, "but I'll tell you what I'll do: you help me as best you can with my corn and I'll do the same with your riddles. How's that?"

"Couldn't be better," Cody replied, and grinning ear to ear he bellied under Mr. Swinney's fence and then held the wires apart for Omalia to climb through. Then he spit on his hands (so he wouldn't raise blisters hoeing) and away he went, breaking the crusty earth and chopping the weeds so Mr. Swinney's corn plants would flourish.

Mr. Swinney put Omalia to work in the popcorn patch because the popcorn plants were smaller than the others and there weren't so many of them.

"Speaking of riddles," Mr. Swinney said after a bit, "here's a good one. What has ears but can't hear?"

"That's the easiest old riddle that ever was riddled," Cody said. "That's your corn."

"Correct," said Mr. Swinney. "And now let me tell you something. If the ones you're fixing to ask me are any harder, you've come to the wrong man to get them answered."

"Golly, I hope not," Cody said, and he stopped hoeing to get his breath and cool off. Hoeing corn in the hot sun was pure hard work. "Try these, now: how can there be a cherry without a stone, a chicken without a bone, a thimble without an end, and a baby without a cry?"

"Whee-yew!" exclaimed Mr. Swinney. "Fierce ones, ain't they?"

"You're mighty whistlin'," Cody agreed. "They're giving me fits."

Mr. Swinney moved his pipe from one side of his mouth to the other. "Let me see now," he said. "A cherry without a stone." He looked down at Cody and said, "It don't hardly seem possible, do it? Any cherry I ever saw had a stone in it."

Cody began to get worried. "What about the boneless chicken, Mr. Swinney? Can you guess that one?"

"Seems like I *ought* to know that one," Mr. Swinney said. He pushed his hat to the back of his head and began scratching to hurry his thinking. "Yes sir, *seems* like a boneless chicken should

be easy, but now I reckon it's got me stumped." Mr. Swinney hooked his thumbs around the shoulder straps of his overalls and looked down at worried Cody. "Here's something I can tell you about riddles," he said. "The harder a riddle riddles you, the easier the answer's going to be."

"Sure," Cody agreed. "This chicken riddle's mighty hard, so what's the easy answer?"

Mr. Swinney sighed. "I wish you'd tell *me*, Cody. It's got me clean stumped. It and that first one. Let me try your third one now — what was it?"

"How can there be a thimble," Cody began, and then he gulped and couldn't say the rest of it because he thought he was going to stump Mr. Swinney a third time.

"Without an end," Mr. Swinney murmured, and he cocked his head on one side and squinted his eyes to slits and looked at a far-off piece of the sky, frowning and pursing his lips around his pipe. He seemed to be thinking about as hard as a man can think.

"How you doin'?" Cody asked impatiently.

Mr. Swinney shook his head and said one word. "Stumped."

Cody swallowed hard. "There's one more," he said hopefully.

"Yeah," said Mr. Swinney, "that one about the baby that doesn't cry. I don't even have to study on that one. I couldn't guess that one in a month of Sundays."

"Gosh, Mr. Swinney," Cody said sadly. "You know just about everything there *is* to know —"

"Except riddles," Mr. Swinney said.

"I warned you I wasn't much account with them. Answerin' 'em, that is. I'm the cat's whiskers at askin' 'em. Listen to this one:

"Houseful
Yardful
You can't catch a
Spoonful.

What do you guess that to be?"

"Houseful, yardful" — Cody tried it over — "you can't catch a spoonful."

"It's something you see every day," Mr. Swinney said helpfully. "You smell it every day and it stings if it gets in your eyes."

"Mosquitoes!" Cody guessed.

"Try again," said Mr. Swinney, laughing.

Cody pressed his lips together and frowned and tugged his hair and stared at his toes and thought and thought. "I'm stumped," he said.

"Stumped, are you?" said Mr. Swinney. "Then try this little old sugarstick of a riddle."

"Hey," said Cody, "first tell me the answer to houseful-yardful."

"Later," said Mr. Swinney. "Let me put this good white-cow riddle to you before it slips my mind:

"Thirty-two white cows
Standing in a stall,
Along comes a red cow
And licks them one and all.

What's that now?"

"Thirty-two white cows!" Cody exclaimed. "Yow! I never in my life saw more than five cows in one place."

Mr. Swinney laughed. "These are riddle cows," he said. "They're not real cows."

Cody did a lot of hard thinking and then suddenly his face brightened up — he had the answer! "That's a white stake fence," he said, "with a red rose rambling over it."

"Makes a mighty pretty picture," Mr. Swinney said, chuckling, "but it ain't the answer."

"Then I'm stumped," Cody said.

"Don't seem you should be on such an easy one," said Mr. Swinney, "but if you are, here's another one."

"Back up," Cody cried. "What's thirty-two white cows in a stall?"

"Tell you later," Mr. Swinney said. "Listen to this nifty one now:

"Two lookers,
Two crookers,
Four down-hangers
And a switch-about."

"Two lookers, two crookers," Cody said, "four down-hangers and a — *golly*, that's the worst one yet!"

Mr. Swinney chuckled. "Easy as falling off a log, Cody. Think a minute. You see a lookers-crookers every day

113

somewhere. You've got one home, and I've got one — I guess everyone on Cumberland Mountain has."

When Mr. Swinney said this, Cody looked all around him hoping he would find the answer, but all he saw besides fence posts and corn was Omalia. Omalia was looking very pleased with herself. "Two lookers, two crookers is an easy one," she said.

Cody looked up at Mr. Swinney. "Stumped," he said. "What's the answer?"

"Already?" Mr. Swinney asked in surprise. "Try this one then —"

"For Pete's sake, hold on!" Cody cried, but he couldn't stop Mr. Swinney.

"Eeno and
Ino,
Fido and
Dido.
Which one was the big dog?"

Cody thought so hard that his face got all twisted like a crumpled-up piece of paper. "Eeno?" he guessed hopefully.

"Try again," said Mr. Swinney.

"Ino?"

"Nope," said Mr. Swinney. "I told you, now you tell me."

"Fido?"

"Fido was the littlest dog," said Mr. Swinney.

"Dido?"

Mr. Swinney shook his head. "Nope, not Dido."

Cody frowned. "I guessed every dog," he said impatiently, "and you noped me every time."

"You guessed every dog but the right one," Mr. Swinney said.

"Well, which one is the big one?" Cody demanded.

Omalia clapped her hands and said brightly, "Cody finally guessed a riddle."

"Hush, Sister," Cody said. And then he pulled his hair and twisted up his face till you wouldn't have known he was Cody Capshaw. "I give up!" he said.

"Why give up when you just named him?" Mr. Swinney asked.

"Named him?" Cody exclaimed.

"You certainly did," said Mr. Swinney.

"If I did," said Cody, "I sure didn't know it." He thought a minute more and then he grabbed his head and rubbed it hard. "Yow!" he complained, "I thought you were going to stop the riddle buzz in my head. It's buzzing worse than ever."

"Turnabout," said Mr. Swinney. "My head's buzzing with the four you riddled me."

"Going to tell me the answers to yours?" Cody asked.

Mr. Swinney looked almost as unhappy as Cody looked. "When you tell me the answers to yours," he said.

"Good night!" said Cody. Then he laughed and said, "And good day!" and he turned and darted out Mr. Swinney's gate.

"Hold on a minute!" Mr. Swinney called.

Cody turned back again, grinning his big grin. It would be just like Mr. Swinney, he thought, to give in and tell him the answers after all.

"Here's you a pip of a riddle," said Mr. Swinney.

"Hey," Cody protested, "no more! You riddled me four and I riddled you four."

"That's right, we're even," said Mr. Swinney, "but this one's a jim-dandy. You wouldn't be happy if you didn't hear it:

"A man without eyes
　Saw plums on a tree.
　He neither took plums
　Nor left plums.
　How can this be?"

Cody stood stock-still for exactly one minute wondering what the answer was. Then he said, "Stumped again, Mr. Swinney!" and ran like a rabbit before Mr. Swinney could throw any more riddles at him.

Omalia had to go some to keep up. When Cody finally slowed down, she caught her breath and said: "That plum one is the first one I don't know the answer to."

"It's about time you couldn't answer one," Cody said.

Just then — "Mmm-BAAW!" a loud deep voice from the side of the road. It was Mr. Swinney's black-and-white cow saying how-do-you-do in cow language.

"Howdy, Drusilla!" Cody said, and he pulled up a handful of crimson clover growing outside the fence and offered it to her.

Drusilla shot out her enormous pink tongue, curled it round the clover, slicked it from Cody's hand as quick as a minute, and went to crumping it in her huge slobbery mouth.

As Cody watched her, he was thinking about his riddles. "Lookers-crook-

short. He tugged a handful of his hair and he thought, "A haircut might be just what I need to help me with this tall thinking I'm doing. Snip some of this thatch off, and my brains will have a chance to work."

And in Mr. Clodfelter's gate he marched (followed, of course, by Omalia) and up onto Mr. Clodfelter's front porch where Mr. Clodfelter kept the pride of his life, a sure-enough barbershop chair with padded leather arms and a great deal of fancy metal-work, and a silver step leading up to the comfortable leather seat. In this fancy chair Mr. Clodfelter clipped and cut and snipped and trimmed folks' hair (long, short, straight, curly, black, white, blond, or red) for a dime a head.

"How are you at answering riddles, sir?" Cody asked as he climbed into the chair.

"I'm twice as good at asking them," Mr. Clodfelter replied. He grabbed up Cody's hair the way you or I would grab a clump of dandelions, and with one snip of his scissors Cody was only

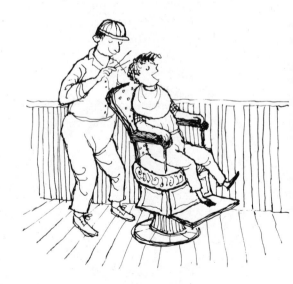

ers," he murmured to himself. And suddenly he had an idea. "That's you," he told Drusilla. "Yes ma'am — two lookers: that's your eyes. Two crookers: that's your horns. Four down-hangers: that's the squirters you give your milk with. And a switch-about: that's your tail switching the flies off. Drusilla, you don't know it, but you're a riddle and I've unriddled you. Thanks for helping me."

Drusilla didn't seem to be the least impressed. All she did was look cow eyes of happiness at Cody for the free clover and go on chewing it.

Nor did Omalia get excited. "You've guessed one," she said, "but you've got eight more."

Cody thought if he kept walking he would maybe meet the answer to another, so down the road he went.

"Mornin', Cody," Mr. Clodfelter called as he saw Cody passing his door. "Want your hair cut today?"

Cody dug his heels in and stopped

116

half as hairy as he had been, coming in Mr. Clodfelter's gate.

"Here's one of my best," said Mr. Clodfelter:

"Round as a biscuit
And deep as a cup.
All the king's horses
Couldn't pull it up.

Know what that is?"

"If I knew," Cody said, "sure as my name's Cody Capshaw I'd zip back up the road and spring it on Mr. Swinney."

"Here's you another pretty fair one," said Mr. Clodfelter, his scissors snip-snip-snipping around Cody's ears like a snapping turtle. "What stands on one leg with its heart in its head?"

"Search me," Cody said. "What?"

"Riddles don't come no easier," said Mr. Clodfelter. "Look out yonder in my garden. What's growing there?"

Cody looked where Mr. Clodfelter was pointing his scissors. "Fourteen cabbages," Cody said, counting them.

"Well?" said Mr. Clodfelter.

"*Cabbages?*" Cody said, his mouth dropping open in surprise.

"A cabbage stands on one leg, don't

it?" Mr. Clodfelter asked, his scissors working over the top of Cody's head.

"That's right," Cody said. "Its stalk is its leg."

"And a cabbage's heart is in the middle of its head, ain't it?" Mr. Clodfelter asked.

Cody began to grin. "Now what's round as a biscuit, deep as a cup?"

"What's it sound like?" Mr. Clodfelter asked.

"Like a biscuit or a cup," Cody said, "or a bucket" — he was looking around for round things to guess — "or a wagon wheel or that tin can there or your water well."

"That's what it is, exactly," Mr. Clodfelter said. He pointed his scissors at his well, out past his cabbages. "There she stands, round as a biscuit, deep as a cup and a good deal deeper, and do you think all the horses in the world could pull a well out of the ground?"

"I reckon not," Cody said, feeling mighty pleased with himself. "I'm getting good — pop me another."

"Tell you what I'll do," said Mr. Clodfelter, peering at Cody over the top of his glasses. "I'll riddle you the pick of all the riddles I ever learned. If you guess it, I'll give you this haircut I'm giving you free for nothing. How's that?"

"Suits me fine," said Cody. "Pull the trigger and let 'er flicker."

"Listen close now," Mr. Clodfelter warned. "Listen as if you were just one big ear, for this is an uncommonly troublesome little old riddle." He rested one arm on the barber chair and cocked one foot over the other for comfort. "We're off," he said:

"In marble walls as white as milk
Lined with skin of softest silk,
Within a fountain crystal clear,
A golden apple doth appear.
No doors there are to this stronghold,
Yet thieves break in and steal the gold."

Cody looked at Mr. Clodfelter. "That's one of these long, hard rascals with an easy answer."

Mr. Clodfelter nodded and looked down at Omalia. "Know it, do you, Sister?"

Omalia had a worried look on her face. "I wish I did," she said. "It's got me going."

"I believe I've got it," Cody said.

"Let 'er flicker," said Mr. Clodfelter.

" 'Marble walls as white as milk,' " Cody said. "That ought to be an egg-shell."

"Umm-hum," said Mr. Clodfelter.

" 'Lined with skin of softest silk,' " Cody said. "That's that little papery stuff you see when you crack an egg."

"I believe you're guessing it," Mr. Clodfelter said.

" 'Within a fountain crystal clear, a golden apple doth appear,' " Cody said. "That's the yellow yolk inside the white."

"Yes sir!" said Mr. Clodfelter. "Looks like I've trimmed your hair for nothing."

" 'No doors there are to this stronghold,' " Cody said. "Sure, who ever heard of an egg having a door?"

"Who be the thieves?" Mr. Clodfelter asked.

"You and me when we break it to eat it," Cody said.

Mr. Clodfelter nodded. "You've unriddled the hardest riddle I ever learned."

"Yippee!" Cody cried.

"What led you to guess it?" Mr. Clodfelter wanted to know.

Cody looked down at Omalia. "Oh," he said airily, "I've heard harder riddles. Thanks for the haircut," he said as he slid out of the chair and hopped down the porch steps.

"Hold on a minute," Mr. Clodfelter called. Cody turned back at the gate. "Long as you're so sharp at guessing hard ones," Mr. Clodfelter said, "maybe you can give me the answer to this A number 1 riddle. I used to know it but I've forgot it."

118

"I'll do what I can for you," Cody said, talking big. After marble-walls-as-white-as-milk, he felt able to unriddle just about any riddle that came along.

"Here we go," said Mr. Clodfelter:

"A man without eyes
Saw plums on a tree —"

"*Ouch!*" Cody said. "'He neither took plums nor left plums. How can this be?'"

"You know it!" Mr. Clodfelter said happily. "What's the answer, if you please?"

"I wish I knew," Cody said. "My friend Mr. Swinney tossed that one at me but he failed to answer it."

"I'm working on it too," Omalia volunteered.

Mr. Clodfelter shook his head sadly. "Whichever one of you hits on it first, you'll surely stop by and tell me, won't you? I've been wrestling with it since the day I forgot it, and it throws me every time."

Down the road marched Cody, his head so full of men without eyes seeing plums on trees that he had no time left to remember something rather important.

And Omalia, also busy with the plum riddle, plumb forgot to remind him.

What was it they both forgot? — why, that Cody had planned to spring his cherry-chicken-thimble-baby riddles on Mr. Clodfelter.

By the time Cody remembered what he had forgotten, he and Omalia were standing at the door to Uncle Jeff Applegate's woodworking shop. "Here's

the man that will know the answers," Cody said half to himself and half to Omalia.

The last time Cody had stopped to visit here, Uncle Jeff had taught him how to spell mischievous and mistletoe and Mississippi and seven miscellaneous other words beginning with miss. It seemed to Cody that riddles ought to be easy for a man who could spell miscellaneous, so into the workshop he popped with a loud "Howdy!"

Omalia followed as close as a shadow.

Uncle Jeff was bottoming a brand new walnut chair, weaving the seat with two long ribbons of white oak.

"Howdy, you two," he returned, glancing up from his chair work. "Been passing the time with old man Clodfelter, have you?"

Cody gaped in astonishment. "How in the world do you know that?" he asked.

"Cody, you've got about as much hair left on your head," Uncle Jeff said,

119

"as I have whiskers on my chin, and that's none whatsoever."

Cody ran his hands over his head. It was true — Mr. Clodfelter had really cleaned him off.

"What's eating you?" Uncle Jeff asked. "The pair of you look plumb tantalized."

"Riddles," Cody told him. "We're riddled."

"Riddles, eh?" said Uncle Jeff. "I knew a few of those things."

"I'll tell you the biggest thing that's wrong with riddles," Cody said in a rush, before Uncle Jeff could start popping any. "Everyone likes to riddle them but nobody likes to come through with the answers!"

"Let's hear one you're having trouble with," Uncle Jeff said.

"Houseful, yardful, you can't catch a spoonful," Cody said. "Mr. Swinney says I see it every day and it stings your eyes and it isn't a mosquito."

"It's smoke," Uncle Jeff said.

"Smoke?" Cody recalled how the smoke from Callie's washpot fire had got in his eyes. He began to grin. "That's right," he said. "Try this one:

Eeno, Ino, Fido and Dido — which one's the big dog?"

"You just named him," Uncle Jeff said.

Cody looked puzzled.

"The last dog you named," Uncle Jeff said.

"Which one?" Cody asked.

"Yup," said Uncle Jeff. "Odd name for a dog, but that's what it was — Which One — and he was the big dog . . . Any more you can't crack?"

"Thirty-two white cows standing in a stall," said Cody. "Along comes a red cow and licks them one and all."

"Well now," said Uncle Jeff, "I've always understood that that little old red cow is your tongue and those little old white cows —"

"Are your teeth!" Cody exclaimed. "Shucks, I guessed it was a fence with a rose growing on it."

Uncle Jeff went back to work on his chair seat. "Here's a riddle you'll guess right off the reel if you don't know it already," he said. "A man without eyes saw plums on a —"

"WHOA!" Cody cried. "Whoa and back up! I've been riddled twice with this one, one time by a man that didn't know the answer and one time by a man that did know it but wouldn't tell it."

"That's the way it is with a good riddle," Uncle Jeff said. "When the riddle's hard, the answer's easy. Try this one:

> "Runs and jumps,
> Stops and humps."

Cody looked at Uncle Jeff. "That *ought* to be a rabbit," he said. "It *sounds* like a rabbit. That's what rabbits do, for I've seen them."

Uncle Jeff laughed. "It *is* a rabbit," he said. "Try this one now:

> "In walking 'cross a field,
> I found something good to eat.
> It was not flesh and it was not bone.
> I kept it till it ran alone."

"Here I go," Cody said. To help himself think, he put up his hand and tried to tug his hair, but Mr. Clodfelter hadn't left him enough to tug, so he had to scratch instead. "Something good to eat," he repeated. "Not flesh, not bone." He looked at Uncle Jeff from the corner of one eye. "A huckleberry," he said.

"Now, Cody!" Uncle Jeff said. "When did you ever see a huckleberry

"Haven't you guessed it?" Uncle Jeff asked in surprise.

"Guessed it?" Cody exclaimed. "If there's a worse riddle going around, I haven't heard it."

"Come to think of it," Uncle Jeff said, "maybe it is a little bit tricky. Look here now — say you were blind. You couldn't see plums on a tree, could you?"

Cody shook his head. He didn't look at Omalia or he would have noticed that she was shaking hers too.

"But if you had *one* eye," Uncle Jeff went on, "you could see them, and one eye is only one eye, it isn't 'eyes.' Same way with the plums. 'He neither took plums nor left plums.' There were only two to begin with, you see. The man took one and left t'other."

"Yow!" Cody cried. "To think I studied and worried and wondered as hard as I did when there's nothing to it."

"Me too," Omalia said.

121

run alone? I told you I kept this riddle till it ran alone."

"But you said it wasn't flesh," Cody protested, "and you said it wasn't bone. How can something that isn't flesh and bone run alone?"

"How about an egg?" Uncle Jeff suggested.

"An egg?" Cody echoed. His eyes grew big as saucers.

"A hen egg," Uncle Jeff said. "It's good to eat and it would run alone if it hatched a chick."

Cody considered this. "I reckon that's the answer," he said. Suddenly he yelled "YOWIE!" and sprang off the chair he was sitting on.

"Something nip you?" Uncle Jeff asked in surprise.

"Nothing nipped me but an idea," Cody said. "*That's* the answer to the boneless chicken! It's boneless when it's in the egg."

"That's right," Uncle Jeff said. "A chick doesn't have bones to amount to anything till it pips its way out of the shell."

Cody grinned one of his widest grins. "That takes care of just about my worst riddle," he said.

"What about the stoneless cherry?" Omalia put in.

Cody frowned. "Yeah, that one," he said. "You reckon you could call a cherry blossom a cherry?" he asked Uncle Jeff.

"I don't see what's to hinder," Uncle Jeff said. "If a chick's a chick while it's in the shell, a cherry ought to be a cherry while it's still in the flower. One's pretty much like the other."

"Gosh, I sure hope that's right," Cody said.

Omalia nodded. "It is."

"Try another one?" Uncle Jeff asked.

"Why not?" Cody said. "I'm getting good."

"Here we go then," said Uncle Jeff. "This one's a lallapalooza:

"Black we are and much admired;
  Men seek for us till they are tired.
  We tire horses, comfort man,
  Guess this riddle if you can."

"Whew!" said Cody. "I'll say it's a lallapalooza."

"I believe your mother sometimes burns it in her stove," Uncle Jeff said.

"Wood?" said Cody.

"*Black* we are and much admired," returned Uncle Jeff.

"Coal!" Cody exclaimed.

"Correct," said Uncle Jeff. "Men seek for us (that's the miners). We tire horses (that's the horses that have to drag the coal out of the mines). We comfort man (coal comforts you and me on a cold day) and there you have it. Here's one more and it's an easy one:

"Round as a biscuit — "

"Shucks, I know what that is!" Cody

said. "That's a well. Mr. Clodfelter riddled me that one and I guessed it in one minute flat."

"Your alarm went off too soon, Cody," Uncle Jeff said. "Listen to the rest of it now:

> "Round as a biscuit,
> Busy as a bee:
> Prettiest little thing
> You ever did see.

Now then, what's *that?*"

"It isn't a well?" Cody asked.

Uncle Jeff shook his head. "All the king's horses couldn't make it a well."

"A bucket," Cody guessed.

"A bucket's round as a biscuit all right," Uncle Jeff admitted, "but I never saw a bucket busy as a bee. Did you?"

"Then I'm stumped," Cody said. "And I thought I was getting good," he added sadly.

Uncle Jeff sat on his new chair to test the bottom he had just finished weaving. Then he pulled on the leather strap running into his pocket and drew out his watch and looked at it. "Gettin' on dinner time," he said and he held his watch up for Cody to read it.

"That's right," Cody said. He looked up at Uncle Jeff, wondering why he kept holding his watch out.

Uncle Jeff grinned. "Round as a biscuit," he said again, "busy as a bee."

"Yow!" Cody exclaimed. "It's not a well and not a bucket but a watch."

"While you're thinking about what the king's horses could do and couldn't do," Uncle Jeff said, "see can you unriddle this one:

> "Hickamore Hackamore
> On the king's kitchen door.
> All the king's horses and
> All the king's men
> Couldn't pull
> Hickamore Hackamore
> Off the king's kitchen door."

This time Cody didn't even take time to scratch his head. He was riddle-whipped. "Give up," he said. "Whoever he is, Hickamore Hackamore's too hardamore for me."

"He's not too hardamore for me!" Omalia announced. "I'm looking right smackamore *at* him."

Cody looked where Omalia was looking and found himself looking at the open door of Uncle Jeff's workshop.

"Yes, indeed," Uncle Jeff said, "Hickamore Hackamore's all over that door."

"All I see," said Cody, "is a great big old yellow smear of sunshine."

"And that's Hickamore Hackamore," Uncle Jeff said. " 'Twould take a whole lot more than the king's horses, don't you think, to pull him off there."

"I reckon," Cody agreed. He broke out grinning. "Hickamore Hackamore's the riddle I'll spring on Mr. Swinney unless you can tell me a harder one."

"Here's you one," said Uncle Jeff, "but you'll guess it right off:

"Has four legs and a foot but can't walk
  Has four legs and a head but can't talk."

Cody scratched his head a minute. "Sounds like it ought to be a bed," he said cautiously. "A bed has four legs and a head and a foot."

Uncle Jeff nodded. "I said you'd guess it," he reminded Cody. "Now try this one. Of all the riddles I know, this is the one I most delight in:

"All over the hills by day,
  Back home at night,
  I sit under the bed
  And gape for bones."

Cody laughed. "That's the easiest riddle I ever heard," he said. "That's Daybreak, my dog!"

"No, sir," said Uncle Jeff.

"It isn't?" Cody was disappointed. "It sure sounds like Daybreak — he's the greatest old bone-eater I ever saw and he's always under the bed."

"I said this riddle *gaped* for bones," Uncle Jeff said. "I didn't say it ate them. When you put your shoe under the bed, it gapes for the bones in your foot."

"My shoe!" Cody thought it over. "Sure enough, that's just what it does."

"Riddle you another one, shall I?" Uncle Jeff asked.

"I'll riddle you a pair," Cody said. "How can there be a thimble that has no end and how can there be a baby that doesn't cry?"

It was Uncle Jeff's turn now to head-scratch and puzzle and this is exactly what he did.

"It's mighty important for me to learn the answers," Cody said. "Tell you why: my mother sings those riddles in a song, and because I never listened to it, I've got to unriddle them myself."

For a pretty good while Uncle Jeff said nothing. Then he looked sadly at Cody and said, "You've stumped me once and you've stumped me twice. Seems to me a thimble wouldn't be a thimble if it had no end and a baby

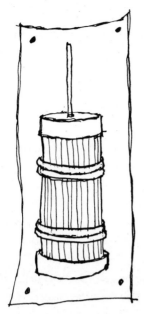

wouldn't be a baby if it didn't cry."

"Gosh, you know so many riddles," Cody said, "and you don't know these two."

"Sure sorry to disappoint you," Uncle Jeff said. "I'll make it up to you by riddling you one more before you go:

"Big at the bottom,
Little at the top.
The jigger in the middle
Goes flippety-flop."

The old man's riddle sounded so funny it made Cody laugh.

"Guessing it, are you?" Uncle Jeff asked.

"Almost nearly but not quite hardly," Cody said.

"How does your mother make her butter?" Uncle Jeff asked.

"She churns it," Cody said.

"In the wooden churn I made for her, doesn't she?" Uncle Jeff asked.

Cody nodded.

"And it's bigger at the bottom than it is at the top," Omalia broke out breathlessly (for she had just this minute unriddled the riddle), "and that old plunging stick goes flippety-flop, flippety-flop going up and down."

"That's it," said Uncle Jeff.

"And that's the one for Mr. Swinney," Cody said. "Thanks for the riddles, Uncle Jeff!"

And with this, Cody popped out the door and began hurrying home. Omalia hurried after him, saying:

"What about the endless thimble? You haven't guessed that one yet."

Cody was too pleased with himself to answer. It struck him he now knew enough riddles to fill a wagon. Probably he knew more riddles than anyone on Cumberland Mountain except maybe Omalia, who had heard them all too. Well, he certainly knew as many riddles as Mr. Swinney and Mr. Clodfelter and Uncle Jeff and Callie and Milt and Omalia combined knew!

"Why bother with that little old thimble riddle," Cody asked himself, "when I know all those other lallapaloozas?"

As he hurried along, he spied a rusty barrel hoop lying beside the road. He snatched up a stick, stood the hoop on its edge, and began running the hoop up the road ahead of him.

"Cody, you haven't guessed the thimble one yet," Omalia said as she hurried to keep up.

Cody had the hoop rolling so fast by the time he came to Mr. Clodfelter's house that all he could do was wave at Mr. Clodfelter and shout out as he ran past:

"The man had one eye and he took one plum and left the other."

Which One was the big dog, and the man who neither took plums nor left plums had one eye and he took one plum and left one, and now what's this:

"Big at the bottom,
Little at the top.
The jigger in the middle
Goes flippety-flop."

"Be hanged if I know," said Mr. Swinney. "What is it?"

Up the road, Cody could hear Callie ringing the dinner bell for him and Omalia. "Come watch my mother make butter and you'll see," he told Mr. Swinney, and he took off in a hurry with his hoop.

Behind him he could hear Mr. Swinney laugh and say, "So it's a churn!"

And behind him he heard Omalia again: "Cody, you've guessed all but one. What about the cryless baby?"

"I'm still stumped on that one," Cody said, racing into the yard. He gave his hoop a final push and sprang up the stairs into the house. He and Omalia were exactly on the dot for dinner.

"Well," said his mother, "did you get those riddles unriddled?"

"Why, sure," Cody said. "There wasn't a really hard one in the bunch."

"He means he unriddled *most* of them," Omalia corrected.

"A rolling thimble has no end," Cody said. "A chicken in the shell has no bone, and a cherry has no stone when it's blooming. That baby's got me stumped. I reckon about the only time a baby doesn't cry is when it's asleep."

Mr. Clodfelter shouted his thanks: "I sure am grateful to you, Cody — that riddle's been keeping me awake nights."

And now the hoop and Cody and Omalia arrived at Mr. Swinney's house. Because Cody had several things to tell his friend Mr. Swinney, he stopped the hoop to catch his breath. And at this very moment a thought hit him. "This hoop," he said to himself, "didn't have an end as long as it was rolling."

He looked around at his sister. "That thimble's like this hoop," he said. "It didn't have an end because it was rolling."

"What's that you say?" Mr. Swinney asked. Mr. Swinney was still hoeing his corn, working near the fence.

Cody looked up at him with a grin on his face as wide as a house. "I got 'em all unriddled," he said. "A cherry has no stone when it's blooming, a chicken has no bone when it's pipping, and a thimble has no end when it's rolling."

"Sounds right," Mr. Swinney agreed.

"And here's the rest," Cody said. "Houseful, yardful: that's smoke. Thirty-two white cows: that's teeth.

"I'll sing you the rest of the song," Callie said, "and you can see how close you are to right."

And these are the words Cody heard:

A cher-ry when it's a bloom-in' it hath no stone,
A chick-en when it's a pipp-in' it hath no bone,
A thim-ble when it's a roll-in' it hath no end,
And a ba-by when it's a sleep-in' it's a no cry-en.

When Callie finished, Cody rubbed his head in relief. For the first time in hours it was no longer tickling.

"Brother," Omalia said, "the next time you hear a song, I guess you'll pay attention to every word of it, won't you?"

"You're mighty whistlin'!" Cody said.

Conclusion:

Unriddling riddles is only one of Cody Capshaw's accomplishments. You can read about his others — all equally hilarious — in the book *This Boy Cody*, by Leon Wilson, published by Franklin Watts, Inc.

MORE FUN WITH RIDDLES

Once you start playing around with riddles, you're apt to run out of good ones before you've had your fill. Here are a few more to keep you going for a while.

What is the best way to keep goats from smelling?
Cut off their noses.

What would you call a man who is always wiring for money?
An electrician.

What kind of clothing lasts the longest?
Underwear, because it is never worn out.

What is worse than finding a worm in an apple?
Finding half a worm.

What question can never be answered by "Yes"?
Are you asleep?

What goes through a door, but never goes in or comes out?
A keyhole.

What kind of shoes are made out of
   banana skins?
Slippers.

What flies up but still is down?
A feather.

What musical instrument should we
   never believe?
A lyre.

What is the hardest thing about learning to ride a bicycle?
The pavement.

What does a hen do when it stands on
   one leg?
Lifts up the other leg.

What did the big firecracker say to the
   little firecracker?
"My pop's bigger than your pop."

What walks over the water and under
   the water, yet does not touch the
   water?
*A woman crossing a bridge over a river
   with a pail of water on her head.*

What is the only thing you can break
   when you say its name?
Silence.

What does a calf become after it is one
   year old?
Two years old.

What would happen if a girl should
   swallow her teaspoon?
She wouldn't be able to stir.

What keeps the moon in place?
Its beams.

What intelligent insects do you find in
   schoolrooms?
Spelling bees.

What is the end of everything?
The letter G.

What is the best thing to take when you
   are run down?
The number of the car that hit you.

What is the highest building in New York?
The public library has the most stories.

Why did the jelly roll?
It saw the apple turnover.

Why is a river rich?
Because it always has two banks.

Why do we buy clothes?
Because we can't get them for nothing.

Why do we all go to bed?
Because the bed won't come to us.

Why is life the hardest riddle?
Because everybody has to give it up.

Why is tennis such a noisy game?
Because each player raises a racket.

Why is an empty purse always the same?
Because there is never any change in it.

Why should a spider make a good out-fielder?
Because it is always catching flies.

Why is an empty matchbox superior to all others?
Because it is matchless.

Why is your nose not twelve inches long?
Because then it would be a foot.

Why would a barber rather shave six men from New York than one from Kokomo?
Because he would get six times as much money.

Why is a coward like a leaky faucet?
Because they both run.

Why is a good student always on the run?
Because he is always pursuing his studies.

Why did Babe Ruth make so much money?
Because a good batter always makes good dough.

Why is it useless to send a telegram to Washington today?
Because he is dead.

129

Why can't it rain for two days continually?
Because there is always a night in between.

Why does an Indian wear feathers in his hair?
To keep his wigwam.

Why is the snow different from Sunday?
Because it can fall on any day of the week.

Why is a policeman the strongest man in the world?
Because he can hold up automobiles with one hand.

Why is the Senate like a book?
Because it has so many pages.

Why is a doctor the meanest man on earth?
Because he treats you and then makes you pay for it.

Why does a bald-headed man have no use for keys?
Because he has lost his locks.

Why do white sheep eat more than black ones?
Because there are more of them in the world.

Why does the Statue of Liberty stand in New York Harbor?
Because it can't sit down.

When are houses like books?
When they have stories in them.

When is a lady not a lady?
When she turns into a drugstore.

When is a sailor not a sailor?
When he's a board (aboard).

When is a hat not a hat?
When it becomes a girl.

When is a door not a door?
When it is a jar (ajar).

When is a man like a pony?
When he is a little hoarse (horse).

When does a boat show affection?
When it hugs the shore.

When is a Scotchman like a donkey?
When he strolls along his banks and braes (brays).

When may we say a student is very hungry?
When he devours his books.

When the clock strikes thirteen, what time is it?
Time to have the clock fixed.

When is a man where he never is and never could be?
When he is beside himself.

When is it socially correct to serve milk in a saucer?
When you give it to a cat.

When a boy falls into the water, what is the first thing he does?
Gets wet.

When a man complains that his coffee is cold, what does his wife do?
She makes it hot for him.

When do 2 and 2 make more than 4?
When they make 22.

When are you not yourself?
When you are a little pale (pail).

When are cooks most cruel?
When they beat the eggs and whip the cream.

When is a clock on the stairs dangerous?
When it runs down and strikes one.

When does a man sneeze seven times?
When he can't help it.

When is coffee like the surface of the earth?
When it is ground.

When can you be said to have four hands?
When you double your fists.

The poor have, the rich require;
The miser spends, the spendthrift saves,
And all men carry to their graves?
Nothing.

Great numbers do our use despise,
But yet, at last they find,
Without our help in many things,
They might as well be blind.
A pair of spectacles.

As I was going to St. Ives,
I chanced to meet nine old wives;
Each wife had nine sacks,
Each sack had nine cats,
Each cat had nine kits.
Kits, cats, sacks and wives,
How many were going to St. Ives?
*Only one. The old wives were going in the
opposite direction.*

I often murmur, but never weep;
Lie in bed, but never sleep;
My mouth is larger than my head,
In spite of the fact I'm never fed;
I have no feet, yet swiftly run;
The more falls I get, move faster on.
A river.

The mother of men was a lady whose name
Read backward or forward, is always the
   same.
Eve.

Four jolly men sat down to play,
And played all night till break of day;
They played for cash and not for fun,
With separate scores for everyone,
Yet when they came to square accounts,
They all had made quite fair amounts.
Can you this paradox explain?
If no one lost, how could all gain?
*The four players were musicians in a
dance orchestra.*

When can your coat pocket be empty
   and yet have something in it?
When it has a hole in it.

When you look around you on a cold
   winter morning, what do you see on
   every hand?
A glove.

When you go to a store for ten cents'
   worth of very sharp tacks, for what
   do you want them?
For ten cents.

What does a man love more than life?
Hate more than death or mortal strife?
That which contented men desire,

Old Mother Twitchhead had but one eye,
And a long tail, which she let fly;
Every time she went over a gap,
She left a bit of her tail in a trap.
A needle and thread.

It wasn't my sister, nor my brother,
But still was the child of my father and
    mother.
Who was it?
Myself.

Instead of complaining when it may rain,
We should do as they do in Spain.
And what is that?
Let it rain.

Conclusion:

The above riddles, and hundreds of others just
as good, are to be found in the book *Riddles, Riddles, Riddles*, by Joseph Leeming, published by
Franklin Watts, Inc.

I'm the name of a country, and strange,
    you'll declare,
If you cut off my head, why, I am still
    there.
Take away my tail twice, but nought you
    will gain,
For e'en though you do, I still will remain.
What country am I?
*Siam. Cut off its head — S — and "I am"
is still there. Then take away A and M,
and I still remains.*

Adam and Eve and Pinch Me
Went down to the river to bathe;
Adam and Eve were drowned,
And who do you think was saved?
*Pinch Me! (When your friend answers
"Pinch me," go right ahead and pinch him,
since he asked for it.)*

133

THE LITTLE RED HEN AND THE GRAIN OF WHEAT

From the beginning of time people have enjoyed listening to stories. Some of these early stories have been handed down from one generation to another and survive today as the familiar folk tales. The industrious little red hen first appeared in old English nursery tales. Today she is still setting a good example for children, who love her very much.

ONE DAY the Little Red Hen was scratching in the farmyard when she found a grain of wheat.

"Who will plant the wheat?" said she.

"Not I," said the duck.

"Not I," said the cat.

"Not I," said the dog.

"Very well then," said the Little Red Hen, "I will." So she planted the grain of wheat.

After some time the wheat grew tall and ripe.

"Who will cut the wheat?" asked the Little Red Hen.

"Not I," said the duck.

"Not I," said the cat.

"Not I," said the dog.

"Very well then, I will," said the Little Red Hen. So she cut the wheat.

"Now," she said, "who will thresh the wheat?"

"Not I," said the duck.

"Not I," said the cat.

"Not I," said the dog.

"Very well then, I will," said the Little Red Hen. So she threshed the wheat.

When the wheat was threshed, she said, "Who will take the wheat to the mill to have it ground into flour?"

"Not I," said the duck.

"Not I," said the cat.

"Not I," said the dog.

"Very well then, I will," said the Little Red Hen. So she took the wheat to the mill.

When the wheat was ground into flour, she said, "Who will make this flour into bread?"

"Not I," said the duck.

"Not I," said the cat.

"Not I," said the dog.

"Very well then, I will," said the Little Red Hen, and then baked a lovely loaf of bread.

Then she said, "Who will eat the bread?"

"Oh! I will," said the duck.

"Oh! I will," said the cat.

"Oh! I will," said the dog.

"Oh, no, you won't!" said the Little Red Hen. "I will." And she called her chicks and shared the bread with them.

MR. AND MRS. VINEGAR

The folk tales often teach a lesson at the same time that they tell a good story. Mr. and Mrs. Vinegar provide us with a classic example of what happens when we become too greedy.

MR. AND MRS. VINEGAR lived in a Vinegar Bottle. It was the nicest vinegar bottle that anyone could have.

One day Mrs. Vinegar was busy sweeping, for she was a very good housewife, when suddenly she knocked the side of the Vinegar Bottle too hard, and klitter, klatter, down came the beautiful Vinegar Bottle over her head.

"Oh dear, oh dear," said Mrs. Vinegar, "what shall I do? What will Mr. Vinegar say?"

Out she ran to the garden, where Mr. Vinegar was working. When Mr. Vinegar saw what had happened he said:

"My dear, don't feel so badly, there are other Vinegar Bottles. Let us take the door of our bottle, carry it on our backs, go out in the world and seek our fortune."

So Mr. and Mrs. Vinegar started out. They traveled all day and at night they came to a forest.

"Now," said Mr. Vinegar, "we will pull the door up into the tree and sleep on it."

After they were nicely settled for the night, along came four robbers. They started to count their money, right under the very tree where Mr. and Mrs. Vinegar were sleeping.

One robber said, "Here are ten pounds for you, Bill."

"Here are ten pounds for you, Jack."

"Here are ten pounds for you, Tom."

At that Mr. Vinegar and Mrs. Vinegar awakened. They were so afraid and trembled so hard, that down came the door on top of the robbers' heads. At

that the robbers ran off, leaving their money behind.

Mr. and Mrs. Vinegar stayed up in the tree until morning, because they were too frightened to come down.

When they came down and picked up the door — they found all the money.

Mr. Vinegar said, "Oh, my dear, our fortune is made."

Mrs. Vinegar said, "Now, Mr. Vinegar, take this money to the fair and buy a nice cow. The cow will give us milk, and we can churn the milk into butter, and sell the butter and buy eggs, and won't we be rich to the end of our days!"

Mr. Vinegar thought this was a very fine idea.

Off he started to the fair, jingling the money in his pocket.

Just as he entered the fair grounds he happened to see a man with a beautiful red cow.

"Oh, dear," said Mr. Vinegar to the man with the red cow, "if I only had that cow I would be the happiest man alive."

"Why," said the man with the cow, "seeing you are a good friend of mine, I don't mind selling the cow to you for forty pounds."

So Mr. Vinegar handed over the forty pounds for the cow.

Instead of going straight home, he walked around the fair grounds showing off his cow. He had not gone very far, when he met a man playing bagpipes. He played such beautiful music that everyone followed him, showering money into his hat.

"Oh, dear," said Mr. Vinegar, "what an easy way to make money. If only I had those bagpipes I would be the happiest man alive."

"Well," said the man with the bagpipes, "seeing you are such a good friend of mine, I don't mind giving you the bagpipes for your cow."

"Oh, thank you," said Mr. Vinegar, and handed over his cow for the bagpipes.

Poor Mr. Vinegar had never played bagpipes before so, instead of playing beautiful tunes, all he could play was squack-squack-squack. The boys and girls, instead of showering pennies upon him, laughed and shouted, I am sorry to say.

It was a cold November day and Mr. Vinegar's fingers grew very numb. On the road he met a man with a nice warm pair of red gloves.

"Oh, dear," said Mr. Vinegar, "if only I had those gloves I should be the happiest man alive."

"Why," said the man with the gloves, "seeing you are a good friend of mine, I do not mind giving the gloves to you for your bagpipes."

"Fine," said Mr. Vinegar, and put on the nice warm gloves.

He walked along happily for some time, humming as he went, but soon became so tired he stumbled over rough bumps on the road. Looking up, he saw a man coming toward him with a good stout stick in his hand.

"What use are these gloves to me?" said Mr. Vinegar. "My feet ache from this rough road."

So he said to the man with the stick, "If only I had that stick I would be the happiest man alive."

"Well," said the man with the stick, "seeing you are a good friend of mine, I do not mind giving you the stick for those gloves."

"Fine," said Mr. Vinegar, and traded the gloves for the stick.

Now a parrot was up in a tree and, seeing what had happened, he called out,

"Oh, foolish Mr. Vinegar had forty pounds and bought a cow,

"Traded the cow for bagpipes,

"Traded the bagpipes for a pair of gloves,

"Traded the gloves for a stick that you could have cut from any tree,

"Foolish Mr. Vinegar."

Mr. Vinegar, hearing this, became so angry that he threw the stick into the tree.

When he came back to Mrs. Vinegar without money, cow, bagpipes, gloves, or stick, Mrs. Vinegar scolded him so hard that he was very sorry that he had not driven the cow straight home.

So this is the story of Mr. and Mrs. Vinegar.

Conclusion:

These versions of "The Little Red Hen and the Grain of Wheat" and "Mr. and Mrs. Vinegar" are from *Chimney Corner Stories, Tales for Little Children*, collected and retold by Veronica S. Hutchinson, and published by G. P. Putnam's Sons. Some of the other good stories in this collection are "Henny Penny," "The Old Woman and Her Pig," "The Three Billy Goats Gruff," "The Three Pigs," and "The Elves and the Shoemaker."

TEENY-TINY

Nonsense is a popular ingredient of the folk tale, for people have always loved to laugh. This story of a teeny-tiny woman has delighted generations of boys and girls.

ONCE UPON A TIME there was a teeny-tiny woman who lived in a teeny-tiny village. One day this teeny-tiny woman put on her teeny-tiny bonnet and went out of her teeny-tiny house to take a teeny-tiny walk. And when the teeny-tiny woman had gone a teeny-tiny way she came to a teeny-tiny gate; and the teeny-tiny woman opened the teeny-tiny gate and went into a teeny-tiny field. And when the teeny-tiny woman had gone into the teeny-tiny field she saw a teeny-tiny bone under a teeny-tiny tree, and the teeny-tiny woman said to her teeny-tiny self, "This teeny-tiny bone will make me some teeny-tiny soup for my teeny-tiny supper."

So the teeny-tiny woman put the teeny-tiny bone into her teeny-tiny pocket and went home to her teeny-tiny house. And when the teeny-tiny woman got home to her teeny-tiny house she was a teeny-tiny tired, and she went up her teeny-tiny stairs to her teeny-tiny chamber and put the teeny-tiny bone into a teeny-tiny cupboard. Then she went to sleep in her teeny-tiny bed, and when she had been asleep a teeny-tiny time she was awakened by a teeny-tiny voice from the teeny-tiny cupboard which said:

"Give me my bone!"

And the teeny-tiny woman was a teeny-tiny frightened. So she hid her teeny-tiny head under the teeny-tiny clothes and went to sleep again. And when she had been asleep for a teeny-tiny time, the teeny-tiny voice cried out again from the teeny-tiny cupboard a teeny-tiny louder:

"Give me my bone!"

This made the teeny-tiny woman a teeny-tiny more frightened. So she hid her teeny-tiny head a teeny-tiny farther under the teeny-tiny clothes.

And when the teeny-tiny woman had been asleep again a teeny-tiny time, the teeny-tiny voice from the teeny-tiny cupboard said again a teeny-tiny louder:

"Give me my bone!"

And the teeny-tiny woman was a teeny-tiny more frightened; but she put her teeny-tiny head out of the teeny-tiny clothes and said in her loudest teeny-tiny voice:

"TAKE IT!"

THE FROG PRINCE

When we speak of "fairy tales" most of us mean stories of enchantment. Often a prince or princess has been placed under a magic spell which can be broken only by some act of love or kindness.

THE FROG PRINCE

IN THE GOOD OLD TIMES when it was still of some use to wish for the thing one wanted, there lived a King whose daughters were very beautiful, but the youngest was so lovely that the sun himself, who had seen so much, wondered at her beauty each time he looked at her.

Near the royal castle there was a great dark wood, and in the wood under an old linden tree was a well. When the day was hot, the King's daughter used to go into the wood and sit by the edge of the cool well; and if the time seemed long, she would take out a golden ball and toss it up and catch it again. This was her favorite pastime.

It happened one day that the golden ball, instead of falling back into the maiden's little hand, dropped to the ground near the edge of the well and rolled in.

The King's daughter followed it with her eyes as it sank, but the well was deep, so deep that the bottom could not be seen. Then she began to weep, and she wept and wept, as if she could never be comforted.

While she was thus weeping she heard a voice saying to her: "What is the matter, King's daughter? Your tears would melt a heart of stone."

When she looked to see where the voice came from, she saw a frog stretching his thick ugly head out of the water.

"Oh, is it you, old waddler?" she said. "I weep because my golden ball has fallen into the well."

"Never mind, do not weep," answered the frog. "I can help you; but what will you give me if I bring back your golden ball for you?"

"Whatever you like, dear frog," said she, "my clothes, my pearls and jewels, or even the golden crown that I wear."

"Your clothes, your pearls, your jewels and your golden crown are not for me," answered the frog, "but if you would love me, and have me for your companion and playfellow, and let me sit by you at the table, and eat from your plate, and drink from your cup, and sleep in your little bed — if you will promise all this, then I would dive under the water and bring your golden ball to you."

"Oh, yes," she answered, "I will promise all, whatever you want, if you will only bring me back my golden ball."

She thought to herself: "What nonsense he talks! As if he could do anything but sit in the water and croak with the other frogs, or could be anyone's companion!"

But the frog, as soon as he had heard her promise, drew his head under the water and sank down out of sight. In a little while he came up again with the ball in his mouth, and he threw it on the grass.

The King's daughter was overjoyed to see her plaything again, and she caught it up and ran off with it.

"Stop, stop!" cried the frog. "Take me up too; I cannot run as fast as you."

But it was of no use, for croak as loud as he might, she would not listen to him, but ran quickly home and very soon forgot all about the poor frog, who had to plunge again to the bottom of the well.

The next day when the King's daughter was sitting at the table with the King and all the court, eating from her golden plate, there came a sound of something creeping up the marble steps, pitter patter. Then there came a knocking at the door, and a voice cried: "Youngest King's daughter, let me in!"

She ran to see who it could be, but when she opened the door and saw the frog sitting outside, she quickly closed the door again and went back to the table, feeling very uneasy.

The King noticed how quickly her heart was beating and said: "My child, what are you afraid of? Is there a giant standing at the door ready to carry you off?"

"Oh, no!" said she, "not a giant, but a horrid frog."

"And what does the frog want?" asked the King.

"Oh, dear father," answered she,

"when I was sitting by the well yesterday, playing with my golden ball, it fell into the water, and while I was crying because I had lost it, the frog came up and promised to bring it back to me if I would let him be my companion. I never thought that he would leave the water and come after me; but now he is outside the door and he wants to come in to me."

Then the frog knocked a second time and cried:

"Youngest King's daughter,
Open to me;
By the well water
What promised you me?
Youngest King's daughter,
Now open to me."

Then the king said: "That which you promised you must perform; so go now and let him in."

So she opened the door and the frog hopped in, following at her heels till she reached her chair.

Then he cried: "Lift me up to you on the table."

She refused until her father told her to do it.

When the frog was on the table, he said: "Now push your golden plate a little nearer, so that we may eat together."

She did as he asked, but everyone could see that she did so unwillingly.

The frog greatly enjoyed the meal, but every morsel the Princess ate seemed to stick in her throat.

At last the frog said: "I have had enough now, and as I am very tired, you must carry me up to your room and put me in your silken bed, that I may go to sleep."

Then the King's daughter began to weep, because she did not want the cold frog to sleep in her little bed.

But the King said firmly: "What you promised you must perform."

So she picked him up with her finger and thumb, and carried him upstairs and placed him in a corner.

But he said: "I am tired and want to sleep; put me in your silken bed."

The Princess most ungraciously did so, crying, "Now will you be quiet, you horrid frog?"

At that he ceased to be a frog and all at once became a charming Prince with beautiful kind eyes.

Then he told her how a wicked witch had turned him into a frog and that no one but a King's daughter could release him from his enchantment.

It came to pass that, with her father's consent, the Princess married the Prince, and their wedding was celebrated with great joy throughout the kingdom.

Conclusion:

These versions of "Teeny-Tiny" and "The Frog Prince" are from *Fireside Stories,* selected and edited by Veronica S. Hutchinson, and published by G. P. Putnam's Sons. Some of the other good stories in this collection are "The Kettle That Would Not Walk," "The Foolish Timid Rabbit," and "The Wonderful Pot."

BEAUTY AND THE BEAST

Here is a tale of enchantment whose origin is buried in the past. Different versions of this story appear in the folk literature of several countries. It is believed that such stories were spread by travelers who journeyed from one tribe to another long ago.

LONG AGO there lived a merchant whose ships sailed the seven oceans. For many years they brought him riches from as far away as China and the golden islands of the tropic seas. But one day a great storm arose. The waves tossed higher than the hills. The merchant's ships were all drowned, and his riches with them. He had nothing left in the world but his three daughters.

"My poor girls," he said, "I shall have to leave you alone while I go forth into the world to seek my fortune all over again. But I shall soon return, and you must tell me what presents you want me to bring you."

The first daughter was proud. She asked for a fine coach in which to ride to town. The second daughter was vain. She asked for golden combs to wear in her hair. But the youngest, who was called Beauty, said,

"I want only your safe return, Father. However, if you must bring me a present, pick me a rose. There is nothing that would please me more."

The merchant traveled many miles and many days without finding the fortune he sought. At last, tired and discouraged, he turned back. He had traveled only a short way when he came to a forest where he remembered only open fields in days gone by.

"These trees have grown faster than trees should grow," he said to himself. "The forest must be enchanted. Perhaps it is full of dangers."

But since he could not find a road around it, he had to follow the path through it.

For days he walked in the deep, dark forest without seeing anything but some deer feeding afar off. At last he came to a castle that was entirely surrounded by roses of every kind and color. Thinking to beg a rose for Beauty, he knocked at the door.

Immediately the door swung open, creaking and groaning as though it had not had the pleasure for a long time. But when the merchant entered the castle, there was nobody there. Not a voice did he hear. There were no footsteps.

"Since there is nobody here, nobody will care if I rest awhile," he said to himself.

With that he strode to the end of the great hall where a crackling fire was burning. In front of it was a couch covered with a bear's skin. It looked so comfortable that he lay down on it. Before many minutes he was sound asleep.

He had slept only a short while when he heard a voice calling him to wake up. Opening his eyes, he saw a table spread with all sorts of good things to eat. But still the hall was empty.

"Since there is nobody here, nobody will complain if I eat this food," he said to himself.

So he ate every bit of food on the table. Then he lay down to sleep again.

When next he awoke the whole night was gone and part of the morning. The sweet air blew in the door. It bore the perfume of roses.

"I have neither coach nor golden combs for my two older daughters," he said to himself. "But I shall pick a rose for Beauty."

And with that he went into the garden.

The roses were so many, and all so beautiful, that he could not make up his mind which one to pick. Then one caught his sleeve with its thorns and said,

"Pick *me*."

It was a dark red rose, more beautiful than any. The merchant broke it gently from the bush.

He was about to carry the flower away when he felt the ground tremble as with an earthquake. Then he heard a roaring like that of a hundred lions. Out of the forest came a terrible Beast.

"So you repay my hospitality by stealing my roses!" roared the Beast. "For that you must die before the sun sets."

The poor merchant fell on his knees and begged,

"Spare me! Spare me! My three daughters are alone in the world. Anything I have is yours if only you will let me return to them."

"Return, then!" roared the Beast. "But as payment for your life, you must send one of your daughters to me. I shall treat her gently, never fear."

With that the Beast went roaring back to the forest.

The merchant made his way home with the heaviest heart you can imagine. He had only sad looks for his daughters. When they asked him how he had fared on his journey, he could only shake his head.

At last Beauty, who was as kind as

she was beautiful, crept to his side and
said,

"Father, something is troubling you,
I know. As I love you, let me share
your sorrow."

So the merchant told Beauty about
the Beast. At first she was all tears, as
any girl would be. But at last she dried
her tears and said,

"Father, let me go to the Beast. I
shall treat him so gently that he will not
dare to harm me."

The merchant was horrified. Beauty
was his favorite daughter. He could not
hear and he would not hear of her going. He would go back to the Beast
himself and beg him to devour him.

But Beauty asked,

"What would we three do alone in
the world? Better that one should go
and two should stay, than that three
should be left fatherless."

At last the merchant agreed to let
Beauty go. She packed all her dresses
and her silver thimble in a little trunk
and set out for the enchanted forest.

She was footsore and very tired when
at last she came to the castle in its
garden of roses. The door stood open
and she entered. In the great hall there
was nobody about. But there was a fire
burning merrily at the far end, and in
front of the fire there was a little couch
covered with the whitest ermine.

Beauty put down her trunk and lay
down on the couch and fell fast asleep
in no time.

When she awoke the hall was filled
with music. The perfume of the roses
blew in through the open door. She
sat up and saw beside her a table
spread for two. At one end was a little

chair all trimmed with ribbons and
roses. At the other end was a perfectly
tremendous chair made of the strongest oak.

Beauty sat down in the little chair
to wait for what would come. Before
long she heard a pad-pad-padding in
the forest. There came the Beast for
his dinner. He came through the courtyard and into the hall and sat himself
down in the tremendous chair.

"Do not be afraid of me, Beauty,"
he said in his big, gruff voice.

Beauty was very much afraid, but
she did not want to hurt the Beast's
feelings by saying so. When food appeared by magic on her plate, she ate
it as though it were the most natural
thing in the world. When milk filled
her silver cup, she drank it. The Beast
did not speak to her again, and little
by little she grew less afraid.

When they had finished eating, the
Beast drew his chair to the fire. He
took a long pipe out of his pocket and
smoked it. Then in his big, gruff voice
he said "Good night," and went pad-
pad-padding back to the forest.

"Poor Beast!" thought Beauty. "He
must sleep on the ground while I sleep
on an ermine couch."

And her tears fell for him as she laid herself down and went to sleep.

The next morning the Beast came again from the forest, bringing a golden bird. The bird flew to Beauty's finger and perched there, singing.

"Do not be afraid of me, Beauty," said the Beast, as before.

"I am not afraid," said Beauty. "But I miss my sisters, and my good, kind father."

The Beast sighed and padded back to the forest.

"Poor Beast!" thought Beauty. "He is lonelier than I."

And her tears fell again.

From that time on, the Beast came every morning with a gift in his furry paws. Sometimes the gift was a flower, and sometimes a colored stone. Once it was a rich brown honeycomb, plucked from a wildwood tree. And once it was a young red fox that frisked like a dog.

As time went on, Beauty grew used to the Beast. He did not seem so ugly and fearsome as he had at first. But he was very ragged and dusty from living in the forest.

"Poor Beast!" said Beauty one day. "I must brush and mend your coat."

And she brushed his coat until it shone. Then she brought her thimble from her trunk and found needle and thread in a drawer. As carefully as though she were sewing her wedding dress she mended the Beast's coat.

"Truly you are no longer afraid of me!" he said joyfully.

"I am not afraid of you," said Beauty, "but I miss my sisters and my good, kind father."

The Beast sighed and went padding back to the forest.

In truth Beauty did miss her sisters and father. She missed them more and more. The time came when she could not stand it to be away from them another day.

"Please let me go home," she begged. "I want only to see my father and sisters one more time. I promise to come back to you in three days and never leave you again."

"I have done everything in my power to make you happy," said the Beast sadly. "I cannot refuse you anything, even this. Go to your father and sisters if you will. I shall wait for you three days."

For a parting gift the Beast gave Beauty a little silver mirror. She packed it in her trunk with her thimble and her dresses, and then she set out for home.

When at last she arrived there her father and sisters were overjoyed. They had thought that the Beast had devoured her long ago. When she told them of the Beast's kindness, they threw up their hands in wonder. But when she showed them the silver mirror, and told them of the singing bird and the small red fox, her sisters suddenly grew jealous.

"Surely the Beast means to fatten you up so that he can devour you later," they said. "Do not go back to him. You know that he cannot follow you out of the enchanted forest. He would have done so already if he could. Stay with us! Stay with us, Beauty! Stay with us!"

Night and day they begged her to

stay. Night and day she told them she must keep her promise to return to the Beast. At last, on the third day, she unpacked her trunk and hung her mirror on the wall and said she would stay.

That night the Beast came to her in her dreams and said,

"I have waited three days and you have not come."

Beauty awoke trembling with fear. The moon was shining through the window full on the mirror the Beast had given her. In it she saw a dark and terrible garden. The birds had flown from it and the roses were all trampled and broken. Among the broken roses lay the Beast. He was sick and dying.

Beauty's tears fell so fast that she could not look at the sad picture in the mirror. She ran out of the house and down the road and through the enchanted forest. At last she came to the castle.

"Beast! Dear Beast!" she called.

There lay the Beast in the garden, just as she had seen him in the mirror.

She knelt beside him and lifted his head in her arms and said through her tears,

"You must not die, for I have come back to you."

The Beast groaned and opened his eyes. When he saw Beauty he gave a great cry and leaped to his feet. His ugly coat fell off, and there stood a handsome Prince, the handsomest Beauty had ever seen. The roses stood up and began to bloom again, the forest shrank away, and the castle stood on a pleasant hill with fields and meadows all around it.

Then the Prince told Beauty that he had been enchanted for seven years and forced to live as a beast. The enchantment was so strong that only the tenderness of a maid as beautiful as a rose could break it.

"You have saved me, Beauty," said the Prince. "My castle and all my lands are yours if you will marry me."

So Beauty married the Prince, and there were no happier people in the land that day.

PUSS-IN-BOOTS

A LONG TIME AGO there was a man who died and left three sons. To one he left his house, to another his fields. But to Jack, the youngest, he left only the cat that prowled the barn.

Poor Jack was in despair. He could think of no way to make a living with a cat.

"I can only kill it and use its fur for a jacket," he said to himself. "But it is so small it will not cover very much of me."

When the cat heard this he gave a loud *meow* and jumped on Jack's shoulder.

"Don't kill me," he said in Jack's ear. "Give me a jacket and boots like a man, and you will not be sorry in the end."

Jack knew he had little enough to lose. He gave the cat a jacket and high boots and a hat to wear with them. The cat put them on, threw an empty sack over his shoulder, and set off down the long white road.

He had not gone very far when he saw a house. Behind the house was a garden of fresh lettuce. The cat knocked at the door. When the farmer's wife opened it he said,

"My master, the Duke of Willowonder, wants a salad for his lunch. If you will spare me a handful of your green lettuce, he will reward you well some day."

The farmer's wife was only too happy to give the cat what he asked. The cat stuffed the lettuce in his sack and set off once more down the road.

At last he came to a field that was full of rabbit holes. He chose the largest and placed the sack beside it. Then he lay down beside the sack and pretended to go to sleep.

Presently a fat rabbit came out of

the hole and began to sniff at the lettuce in the sack. First it poked its nose inside the sack and then it poked its head. Finally there was nothing left outside but its cottontail.

As soon as the rabbit was well inside the sack nibbling at the lettuce, the cat leaped up, grabbed the sack closed, and slung it over his shoulder.

Away he went, down the long white road and up and down dale until he came to the last hill but one. There stood the King's palace. The cat strode into the courtyard with the sack over his shoulder and shouted,

"Hear! Hear! There is a cat come to see the King!"

The butler stuck his head out the window to see what the noise was about. The sight of a cat dressed like a man frightened him out of his wits. He pulled in his head and ran to the King.

"Please, your Majesty," he said in a trembling voice, "there's a puss-in-boots down there who says he has come to see you."

"Show him in," said the King. "That is a sight I never saw and I must see it."

So the butler brought the cat to the King and the King sat on his tallest throne and looked at the cat. He looked him up and he looked him down, and at last he said,

"This is indeed a sight worth seeing. But what is that kicking the sack over your shoulder, puss?"

"This is a fine fat rabbit my master has sent for your dinner," said the cat. "He begs you to accept it."

"And who is the master of a puss-in-boots?" asked the King.

"Why, he is the Duke of Willowonder, of course," said the cat.

"Of course," said the King. "Of course. Ask him to dine with me one day."

The next day the cat caught two fat ducks and put them in his sack and carried them to the palace. Once more he stood in the courtyard and shouted,

"Hear! Hear! There is a cat come to see the King!"

The butler was twice as frightened as before. He ran to the King and said, "Your Majesty, that puss-in-boots is back again."

"If I saw that sight once, I never saw it twice," said the King. "Show him in."

So the butler brought the cat to the King, and the King was delighted.

"What is that kicking your sack over your shoulder today?" he asked.

"Two fat ducks," said the cat. "My master begs you to accept them for your dinner."

"I have never met your master," said the King. "I should like to meet him. Ask him to dine with me one day."

"I shall," said the cat, and off he went.

When he reached home he said to Jack,

"Tomorrow the King will pass this way going to the fair. You must do exactly as I say, and never ask me why. And be sure to remember this — you are no longer Jack. You are the Duke of Willowonder."

The next day, very early, the cat heard the rumble of the King's coach on the road. Quickly he ran to Jack and said,

"Run, run, and bathe in the river. But leave your clothes hidden under a stone."

Jack did as he was told, even though the river was very cold and he did not care for bathing. The cat put on his boots and jacket and his hat and stood by the roadside. When the coach came in sight he waved and shouted with all his might,

"Help, help! My master, the Duke

of Willowonder, is drowning in the river!"

The coachman pulled up his horses and shouted to the King,

"Here's a puss-in-boots who says his master is drowning in the river!"

"H'mm," said the King. "I've seen that puss before. Go quickly and rescue his master."

Then he raised the window beside him and said to the cat,

"Bring your master to me as soon as he is rescued."

"Alas, I cannot," said the cat. "He is not presentable. His clothes drowned before he did, and they are already on their way down the river."

"That is easily fixed," said the King. And he sent one of his guards back to the castle for a new suit of clothes.

Meanwhile Jack had been dragged out of the river by the coachman. He stood shivering behind a bush, waiting for the cat to tell him what to do next. When the cat came with the clothes the guard had brought, Jack put them on quickly. They were made of the finest cloth and they fitted him like his own. By the time he had buttoned all the gold buttons and flung the velvet cape over his shoulder he felt like a Duke, and even grander. Holding his head high, he went to meet the King.

Jack looked so fine in his new clothes that the King introduced him to his daughter, the Princess, who was riding with him in the coach. The Princess thought that Jack was the handsomest young man she had ever seen. She asked her father to invite him to ride to the fair with them. This the King did, and Jack climbed into the coach.

The coachman asked the cat to climb up beside him, but the cat said he would rather run ahead. Then he ran like the wind until he was out of sight of the coach.

The first thing he came to was a fine field of barley. There were two men standing by to guard it. The cat said to them,

"The King is coming along the road. He will stop to ask whose field this is. If you do not say that it belongs to the Duke of Willowonder, I shall come back here and chop you into bits."

The field really belonged to a cruel ogre who lived just over the hill. The men guarding the field were his servants. They were so used to being told that they would be chopped into bits that they thought nothing of it. But they were so used to obeying that they said they would obey the cat.

The cat ran on until he came to a fine herd of cattle feeding on thick green grass. There were men with them, herding them around.

"Hallo, there!" shouted the cat. "The King is coming along the road. He will stop to ask whose cattle these are. If you do not say they belong to the Duke of Willowonder, I shall come back and bite you into pieces."

The herdsmen also worked for the cruel ogre. They were so used to being told that they would be bitten into pieces that they thought nothing of it. But they said they would do as the cat told them.

Then the cat ran on until he came to the castle of the cruel ogre. It was a beautiful big castle, all surrounded with gardens and fruit trees. There was

151

a courtyard paved with gold, and a fountain with a rainbow all around it. The cat strode boldly through the gate and knocked at the castle door.

"Hallo, there!" he shouted. "Here is a cat come to see the master of this castle."

Immediately the ogre opened the door and growled,

"Where did you get those boots?"

"They were given to me by my master, the Duke of Willowonder," said the cat. "Surely you have heard of him?"

"What are you doing here?" growled the ogre.

"Just passing by," said the cat. "But I could not pass by the castle of so noble a lord without stopping to pass the time of day."

"Then come in and pass it," said the ogre.

He led the way into a great hall furnished with the most beautiful things. They were much too good for an ogre. The cat sat down in front of the fireplace and curled his tail around him.

"I have heard," he said, "that you are a most wonderful fellow. Is it true that you can change yourself into any animal you choose?"

"I can do that," growled the ogre.

"I should have to see it to believe it," said the cat.

"Believe it, then!" roared the ogre, changing himself into a tiger.

The cat was so frightened that he leaped through the window into a tree.

This amused the ogre so much that he rolled over and laughed and laughed until he split his tiger skin. Then he was an ogre again.

The cat came down out of the tree and said,

"That was good enough. But it cannot be too hard for a big fellow like you to change himself into a tiger. Now if you had changed yourself into something small, like a bird or a mouse, I should have been really surprised."

"I can do that too," said the ogre, and he changed himself into a little gray mouse.

It was just what the cat had been waiting for. With one leap he fell on the mouse and gobbled him up.

All this while the King and Jack and the Princess were rolling along the road in the King's coach. They came to the field of barley. Seeing the men on guard, the King asked the coachman to stop.

"This is a beautiful field of barley," he said to the men. "To whom does it belong?"

"It belongs to the Duke of Willowonder," said the men with one voice.

"Why, Duke," said the King. "I did not know you owned a field as fine as that."

Jack said nothing, for he could think of nothing to say.

They went rolling along the road and rolling along it until they came to the men herding the cattle. The King asked the coachman to stop.

"Whose cattle are those?" he asked the herdsmen.

"They belong to the Duke of Willowonder," said the herdsmen.

"By my beard!" said the King to Jack. "I never dreamed you owned such fine cattle as these."

So they rolled along and they rolled

along until they came to the ogre's castle. Flags were flying all over the roof, and a hundred soldiers were standing at salute.

"That castle is bigger than mine!" exclaimed the King. "The flags wave higher, and the soldiers stand straighter. Whoever in the world lives there, I wonder?"

And he ordered the coachman to stop.

Just then the cat came bounding down the driveway in his boots.

"Welcome to the castle of the Duke of Willowonder!" he shouted.

The King turned to Jack in great surprise.

"My boy," he said, "you are modesty itself. Not once since you entered my coach have you boasted of your great wealth. And now I am so curious to see the whole of this great castle of yours that I have lost all interest in going to the fair."

So Jack and the King and the Princess got down from the coach and went into the castle. There they found a great feast spread and waiting.

After they had dined, the King said to Jack,

"I do not know your plans for the future, but I should be very happy if you would be my son-in-law."

That was exactly what Jack had had in mind ever since he laid eyes on the Princess.

"That I should like well enough," he said.

The Princess said she would like nothing better.

It was agreed that Jack should come to the palace the very next day and marry the Princess. Then the King drove home with her to await his coming.

As soon as the coach had disappeared down the road Jack turned to the cat.

"Faithful friend!" he said. "To think that once I planned to kill you and use your fur for a jacket! When I have married the King's daughter I shall make you lord over all this land. You will be known as His Honor, the Lord High Cat."

"No," said the cat. "Now is the time when you must kill me. Take a silver knife and cut off my head."

"That I will never do!" said Jack.

"You will be doing me the greatest favor," said the cat. And he begged and begged until Jack said he would cut off his head.

No sooner had Jack touched the neck of the cat with the knife than there came a great clap of thunder and the cat disappeared in a tower of blue smoke. There in his place stood a handsome Prince.

"You have freed me from the enchantment the ogre put on me long ago," said the Prince. "These lands are mine, and so is this castle. I give them all to you in return for giving me back my true shape. Now I am off to my lands across the sea, which are twice as big and three times as rich as these."

And with that the Prince left, carrying the boots with him for remembrance.

THE BOY WHO WENT TO THE NORTH WIND

This is the Scandinavian version of a story which has several variants in other folk literatures. As in most folk tales, good is rewarded and evil punished.

NILS WAS THE SON of a poor widow woman who was too ill to do anything but lie in bed. Nils was not too bright, but neither was he too stupid. He worked in the garden, and milked the cow, and when he was finished he worked in the house. Somehow he managed to keep food on the table, but there was never very much of it. Most days he and his mother were hungrier than they liked to be.

One day Nils went to the storehouse behind the well to get a handful of flour to make a cake. Just as he started back to the house, *pouff!* came the North Wind and carried the flour away. That was a serious loss. There was no more flour in the storehouse.

Nils ran rubbing his eyes and crying to his mother.

"The flour! The flour!" he cried. "The North Wind has carried it away!"

"Nils," said his mother, "I have told you a hundred times to carry the flour in one hand and cover it with the other. But let us not worry about what is already done. We shall go to bed hungry tonight, and tomorrow you must go to the North Wind and ask him to give you back our flour."

The next day Nils journeyed to the North Wind's cave, northeast of the well by a day and a half. He found the North Wind asleep on the grass. Not wanting to waken him before he had finished his nap, Nils sat down to wait. While he waited he looked around for the flour, but he did not see it anywhere.

At last the grass began to stir. The

154

North Wind rose with a roar and whirled into the trees.

"North Wind! North Wind!" Nils shouted. "Don't blow away. I have come to beg for the flour you carried off."

The North Wind dropped back onto the grass and asked, "What flour? You don't expect me to remember everything I carry off, do you?"

"But it was our only flour," said Nils. "And already my mother and I are hungrier than we like to be."

"Dear me!" said the North Wind. "I am sorry to hear that. But I cannot remember where I dropped your flour, or if I dropped it at all."

The North Wind looked so worried that Nils said,

"Never mind. My mother says not to worry about what is already done. Perhaps you will give me a handful of your own flour to take its place."

"I will not because I cannot," said the North Wind. "And I cannot because I do not have it to give. But I shall give you something a whole lot better."

And with that he whirled away and went streaming into his cave.

In a few minutes he came back, fluttering a square of white cloth.

"Lay this cloth on a table and say, 'Spread yourself, cloth,' and see what you will see," he told Nils.

Nils set out with the cloth. The first day he traveled until he came to an inn with a friendly look. He knocked at the door and the innkeeper let him in.

"I am the son of a poor widow woman," said Nils. "We are both hun-grier than we like to be, but I am not begging for my dinner. I only want to rest in some corner until morning. Then I shall be on my way."

The innkeeper did not like the idea at all. He was afraid that Nils was a thief. But his wife said,

"Husband, forget your fears. Suppose it were our own boy on the road. Would you not be grateful for any kindness shown him?"

The innkeeper thought about this, and finally he said that Nils might sleep in the corner farthest from the fire. The boy wrapped the North Wind's cloth around him for warmth, and settled down to sleep.

No sooner had he closed his eyes than his stomach began to complain that it had not had its supper.

"Alas, stomach, what can I do?" asked Nils. "I do not have a penny in my pocket for a crust of bread."

But his stomach kept on complaining until Nils thought of the cloth the North Wind had given him.

"It is not keeping me warm at all," he thought. "Let us see what will happen if I spread it on a table."

So he crept out of his corner and laid the cloth quietly on the smallest table in the room.

"Spread yourself, cloth," he whispered.

Immediately a big bowl of soup appeared out of nowhere and sat itself down on the table. It was full of potatoes and meat and little green peas. Nils drank it down quickly to quiet his stomach.

As soon as he had finished the soup,

the bowl flew into nowhere and a little round cake with pink icing took its place.

"My!" said Nils. "This is the finest meal I ever tasted!"

He finished every crumb of the cake. Then he thanked the cloth and folded it carefully and laid it away in the corner. Curling himself up beside it, he went to sleep.

All this while the innkeeper had been watching through a hole in the floor upstairs. When he saw the wonderful cloth and what it could do he said to his wife,

"That cloth could make my fortune."

"It could indeed," said his wife, "if it were yours."

"It is mine if I make it mine," said the innkeeper, and he crept downstairs. Without waking Nils he took the cloth and put another in its place.

When Nils woke up he did not know what had happened. He stuffed the useless cloth in his pocket. Then he thanked the innkeeper for letting him stay the night, and set off once more on his journey home. He arrived there about lunchtime, very hungry.

"Have you brought the flour?" asked his mother.

"No, but I have brought something better," said Nils.

With that he spread the cloth on the table and said, "Spread yourself, cloth."

Nothing happened, of course. Nils waited a good long time and then he shouted angrily,

"Spread yourself, cloth!"

Still nothing happened.

"Oh, you foolish boy!" said his mother. "You have been cheated. Go back at once to the North Wind. Return his cloth and tell him to give us our flour instead."

So Nils set forth once more, traveling northeast of the well for a day and a half. He found the North Wind blowing himself out of his cave with a sound like the sea.

"North Wind! North Wind!" Nils shouted. "Don't blow away! The cloth you gave me is no good. Please give me back our flour."

"Dear me! Dear me! Dear *me!*" said the North Wind. "You have been a very careless boy. I am afraid I cannot give you back your flour because I do not have it to give. But I shall give you something better than either the flour or the cloth."

And with that he blew out of the cave a little white goat with silver horns.

"When you are in need, say 'Give, little goat, give,' and see what you will see," said the North Wind. "But mind you keep your eyes open this time."

Then he went roaring off to fill the sails of the ships at sea.

Nils fastened a little string around the goat's neck and led it carefully down the road. When he had traveled half of his journey he came to the inn where he had stopped before. The inn had a different look about it. It was freshly painted and there were new steps leading up to the door.

"The man is doing well," thought Nils. "His customers must be richer and more particular. Perhaps he will not want a poor boy sleeping in the corner."

But he knocked because he had nowhere else to sleep.

"Come in! Come in!" said the innkeeper. "And what have you brought with you this time?"

"Only a goat," said Nils. "But it is a wonderful goat at that. I have only to say, 'Give, little goat, give,' and I shall see what I shall see."

"Bring him in," said the innkeeper. "A goat like that must not be allowed to sleep in the stable."

So Nils curled up in the corner with the goat beside him. But no sooner had he closed his eyes than his curiosity pried them open, saying,

"Why should you wait any longer to see what the goat can do?"

So Nils sat up and said, "Give, little goat, give."

Right away there was such a clatter on the floor! Beside the goat was a pile of gold pieces.

"This is wonderful," said Nils. "Never again shall I work in the garden, and milk the cow, and work in the house."

And he put the gold pieces in his pocket and lay down and went to sleep.

But the innkeeper had been watching again through the hole in the floor. When he saw what happened he said to his wife,

"That goat could make my fortune."

"It could indeed, if it were yours," said his wife.

"It is mine if I make it mine," said the innkeeper.

He put on his softest slippers and crept downstairs. Without waking Nils he emptied the boy's pockets, led off the goat, and put another in its place.

The next morning, without knowing what had happened, Nils set off with the useless goat. He arrived home about suppertime, very hungry.

"Have you brought the flour at last?" asked his mother.

"No, but I have brought something better," said Nils.

With that he took the little string that was around the goat's neck and led the animal to his mother.

"Oh, you foolish boy!" she said. "That is a he-goat. It will not give any milk. We shall have to make room for it in the stable and feed it, and what will become of us then?"

"Oh, but it gives something better than milk," said Nils. And he said, "Give, little goat, give."

The goat gave him a look, but that was all.

Then Nils shouted angrily, "Give, little goat, give!"

At that the goat kicked up its heels and ran into the garden, trampling the beans into the ground.

Nils' mother said, "Go back! Go back to the North Wind with your silly goat and tell him to give us our flour instead."

So Nils took the little string and led the goat sadly away.

For a day and a half he traveled before he came to the North Wind's cave. When he got there the North Wind was busy making a snowstorm, but he took time to listen to Nils' story.

"You are a very, very foolish boy," he said when Nils was through. "Will you never learn? I cannot teach you what your eyes will not see, and I cannot give you your flour because I do not have it. But I shall give you one more chance."

Then he broke a withered branch from a tree and said,

"Here is a stick. When you want it to do what you want it to do, say to it, 'Lay on.' When you want it to stop, say 'Lay off.' But do not come to me again. I have no time for foolish boys."

Once more Nils started homeward, this time with the stick over his shoulder. When he came to the inn he saw that it was no longer an inn, but a house. There were two horses and a carriage in the stable.

"The innkeeper has grown rich while I have grown poorer and poorer," thought Nils. "Surely he will not let me sleep in the corner tonight."

He was just about to turn away when the innkeeper threw open an upstairs window.

"Nils," he called. "Come in and rest yourself."

Nils went in gladly, but this time he kept his eyes open.

The innkeeper rubbed his hands together and stared at the stick over Nils' shoulder.

"What wonder have you brought with you now?" he asked.

"It is not a wonder," said Nils. "It is only an old stick that I picked up on my walk."

And he put it carelessly in the corner where he was to sleep.

The innkeeper rushed upstairs in great excitement.

"The boy has brought only a stick this time," he said. "But I am sure it is the greatest wonder of all."

"It is not your wonder," said his wife.

"It is mine if I make it mine," said the innkeeper.

And he sat himself down by the hole in the floor to watch.

The innkeeper watched nearly the whole night through, but nothing happened. Nils snored away in the corner and the stick stayed where he had put it. At last the innkeeper could stand it no longer.

"I must have that wonder, whatever it is," he said to himself.

Very carefully he crept downstairs and to the corner where Nils lay. He reached over him and took hold of the stick.

But Nils had only pretended to be asleep. He jumped up and shouted to the stick,

"Lay on!"

Immediately the stick began to beat the innkeeper over the back. The innkeeper howled and ran around the room and leaped over the table, but the stick kept right on beating him.

"Call off your stick!" he howled. "If only it will stop beating me I will give you back your cloth and your goat and anything else you ask!"

Then Nils saw that the innkeeper

had had all he deserved, so he said to the stick,

"Lay off."

The stick stopped beating the innkeeper and stood itself in the corner.

And that was how Nils got back his cloth and his goat. He shouldered the stick and hung the cloth on it for a flag. Leading the goat by the little string, he went home to his mother to live happily ever after.

Conclusion:

These versions of "Beauty and the Beast," "Puss-in-Boots" and "The Boy Who Went to the North Wind" are from *The First Book of Fairy Tales*, retold by Elizabeth Abell, and published by Franklin Watts, Inc. Another good story in this collection is "The Miller's Boy and the Cat."

WHY DOGS WAG THEIR TAILS

Early storytellers in the Philippine Islands began their tales with the words "Once in the first times." The custom is still followed by many Filipinos today.

ONCE IN THE FIRST TIMES there was a rich man who lived all alone except for his dog and cat. The man had a daughter, but she lived at a convent several miles away where she was receiving her education. The girl's father loved his daughter very much and took great pleasure in giving her little presents. These he sent to her about once a week by the dog and cat. The dog was very old now and had lost his teeth so that he could not fight. But the cat was strong and clever. However, it was the dog who knew the way to the convent, so both went along on the errand.

The rich man possessed a ring which had magical powers and he decided to send it to his daughter. So one day he called the cat and dog to him and said that they were to take it to the convent. He gave them their orders. To the cat he said, "You are clever and wise so you may carry the ring. But be sure to take the greatest care not to drop it."

To the dog he spoke thus, "You are to accompany the cat because you know the way. But you must both be very careful not to lose the ring, for it is very valuable."

The dog and cat promised their master that they would be most cautious, and they set out at once on the errand.

When they had come to the river over which they had to cross, there was

160

no boat to take them to the other side. The river was wide and very deep but they decided that they would swim across it to reach their destination.

"Give the magic ring to me," said the dog.

"No, indeed," answered the cat. "Did you not hear the master say that he wished me to carry it?"

But the dog put up an argument. "You are not a good swimmer and may let the magic ring fall into the water. I will carry it and it will be safe."

But the cat refused to disobey her master's orders. The two then began to quarrel bitterly, until finally the dog threatened to kill the cat if she did not entrust the ring to his care. So at last the cat, unwillingly, gave in.

There was a strong current in the river and the swimming was very difficult for both animals. They swam for more than an hour, and the dog became exhausted. Then, just before they had reached the other side, the dog dropped the magic ring into the river.

When they reached the bank the dog had to confess to the cat what had happened.

"Now you see, we should have obeyed our master's words!" the cat scolded. "There is only one thing to do.

We shall have to return to our master at once and tell him that you have lost the ring."

The dog agreed, but he was terrified at the thought of facing his master. They swam back across the river and turned their steps homeward. But the closer they came to the house, the more frightened the dog became. And before they reached there, he ran away.

When the cat returned alone, the master was surprised to see her back so soon and to see that she was alone.

"Where is the dog, and why are you back so soon?" he asked.

At first the cat was too frightened to answer. But when the master asked a second time, the cat said, "The dog has run away, master."

"Run away? Indeed, why has he run away?"

Then the man knew that something was wrong. "Where is the ring?" he demanded.

"Pray do not be angry," begged the cat, "and I will tell you what happened. I carried the ring as you told me to do until we came to the river. There was no boat by which we could cross, so we decided to swim. However, the dog insisted that I let him carry the ring, but of course I refused. He was so determined that he threatened to kill me then and there if I did not give it to him. Oh, master, forgive me, for I gave him the ring. We had great difficulty in swimming the strong currents, and when we had reached the opposite side the dog confessed to me that he had dropped the magic ring into the river."

"But where is the dog?" asked the angry man.

"Alas, master, he was so frightened at the thought of facing you after what he had done, that he ran away."

The rich man by this time was so enraged at the dog that he immediately issued a proclamation offering a reward to anyone who should find and return the animal. The dog could be recognized, he stated, by the fact that he was old and had no teeth. And the master declared that when he found the dog he would punish him by cutting off his tail.

Though the people searched for the dog, they never found him. So the rich man ordered all the dogs in the world to join in the search for the missing one. And the dogs searched, but they could not find him.

And so from that day to this whenever a dog meets another dog he asks, "Are you the dog who lost the magic ring?"

Then the dogs both show their teeth

and wag their tails to prove that they are not the old dog whose teeth were gone and whose tail was threatened.

Since that day, too, all cats have been afraid of water and avoid it whenever possible.

Conclusion:

This story has been selected from *Once in the First Times, Folk Tales from the Philippines*, retold by Elizabeth Hough Sechrist, published by Macrae Smith Company. Other good stories in this book include "How the Lizards Got Their Markings" and "The Artificial Earthquake."

JATAKA TALES

The following three fables come from the Jatakas, or Birth-stories, which form one of the sacred books of the Buddhists. They are very ancient, having been handed down by word of mouth.

HOW THE TURTLE SAVED HIS OWN LIFE

A KING once had a lake made in the courtyard for the young princes to play in. They swam about in it, and sailed their boats and rafts on it. One day the king told them he had asked the men to put some fishes into the lake.

Off the boys ran to see the fishes. Now, along with the fishes, there was a Turtle. The boys were delighted with the fishes, but they had never seen a Turtle, and they were afraid of it, thinking it was a demon. They ran back to their father, crying, "There is a demon on the bank of the lake."

The king ordered his men to catch

the demon, and to bring it to the palace. When the Turtle was brought in, the boys cried and ran away.

The king was very fond of his sons, so he ordered the men who had brought the Turtle to kill it.

"How shall we kill it?" they asked.

"Pound it to powder," said some one.

"Bake it in hot coals," said another.

So one plan after another was spoken of. Then an old man who had always been afraid of the water said: "Throw the thing into the lake where it flows out over the rocks into the river. Then it will surely be killed."

When the Turtle heard what the old man said, he thrust out his head and asked: "Friend, what have I done that you should do such a dreadful thing as that to me? The other plans were bad enough, but to throw me into the lake! Don't speak of such a cruel thing!"

When the king heard what the Turtle said, he told his men to take the Turtle at once and throw it into the lake.

The Turtle laughed to himself as he slid away down the river to his old

home. "Good!" he said, "those people do not know how safe I am in the water!"

THE QUARREL OF THE QUAILS

Once upon a time many quails lived together in a forest. The wisest of them all was their leader.

A man lived near the forest and earned his living by catching quails and selling them. Day after day he listened to the note of the leader calling the quails. By and by this man, the fowler, was able to call the quails together. Hearing the note, the quails thought it was their leader who called.

When they were crowded together, the fowler threw his net over them and off he went into the town, where he soon sold all the quails that he had caught.

The wise leader saw the plan of the fowler for catching the quails. He called the birds to him and said, "This fowler is carrying away so many of us, we must put a stop to it. I have thought of a plan; it is this. The next time the

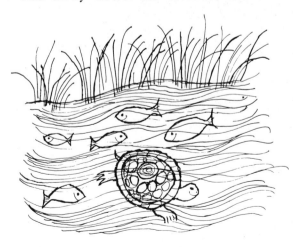

fowler throws a net over you, each of you must put your head through one of the little holes in the net. Then all of you together must fly away to the nearest thorn bush. You can leave the net on the thorn bush and be free yourselves."

The quails said that was a very good plan and they would try it the next time the fowler threw the net over them.

The very next day the fowler came and called them together. Then he threw the net over them. The quails lifted the net and flew away with it to the nearest thorn bush, where they left it. They flew back to their leader to tell him how well his plan had worked.

The fowler was busy until evening getting his net off the thorns and he went home empty-handed. The next day the same thing happened, and the next. His wife was angry because he did not bring home any money, but the fowler said, "The fact is those quails are working together now. The moment my net is over them, off they fly

with it, leaving it on a thorn bush. As soon as the quails begin to quarrel I shall be able to catch them."

Not long after this, one of the quails, in alighting on their feeding ground, trod by accident on another's head. "Who trod on my head?" angrily cried the second. "I did; but I didn't mean to. Don't be angry," said the first quail, but the second quail was angry and said mean things.

Soon all the quails had taken sides in this quarrel. When the fowler came that day he flung his net over them, and this time, instead of flying off with it, one side said, "Now, you lift the net," and the other side said, "Lift it yourself."

"You try to make us lift it all," said the quails on one side. "No, we don't!" said the others. "You begin and we will help," but neither side began.

So the quails quarreled, and while they were quarreling the fowler caught them all in his net. He took them to town and sold them for a good price.

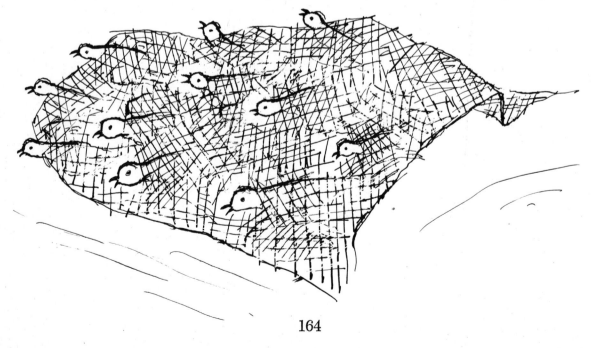

164

THE FOOLISH, TIMID
RABBIT

Once upon a time, a Rabbit was asleep under a palm tree.

All at once he woke up, and thought: "What if the world should break up! What then would become of me?"

At that moment, some Monkeys dropped a coconut. It fell down on the ground just back of the Rabbit.

Hearing the noise, the Rabbit said to himself: "The earth is all breaking up!"

And he jumped up and ran just as fast as he could, without even looking back to see what made the noise.

Another Rabbit saw him running, and called after him, "What are you running so fast for?"

"Don't ask me!" he cried.

But the other Rabbit ran after him, begging to know what was the matter.

Then the first Rabbit said: "Don't you know? The earth is all breaking up!"

And on he ran, and the second Rabbit ran with him.

The next Rabbit they met ran with them when he heard that the earth was all breaking up.

One Rabbit after another joined them, until there were hundreds of Rabbits running as fast as they could go.

They passed a Deer, calling out to him that the earth was all breaking up. The Deer then ran with them.

The Deer called to a Fox to come along because the earth was all breaking up.

On and on they ran, and an Elephant joined them.

At last the Lion saw the animals running, and heard their cry that the earth was all breaking up.

He thought there must be some mistake, so he ran to the foot of a hill in front of them and roared three times.

This stopped them, for they knew the voice of the King of Beasts, and they feared him.

"Why are you running so fast?" asked the Lion.

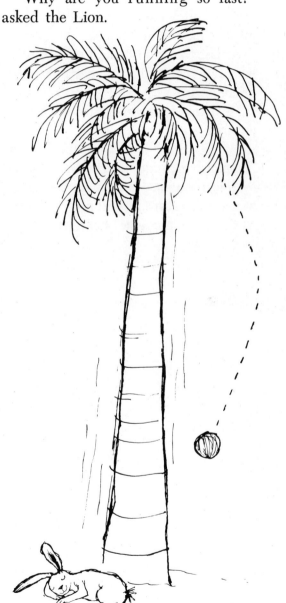

165

"Oh, King Lion," they answered him, "the earth is all breaking up!"

"Who saw it breaking up?" asked the Lion.

"I didn't," said the Elephant. "Ask the Fox — he told me about it."

"I didn't," said the Fox.

"The Rabbits told me about it," said the Deer.

One after another of the Rabbits said: "I did not see it, but another Rabbit told me about it."

At last the Lion came to the Rabbit who had first said the earth was all breaking up.

"Is it true that the earth is all breaking up?" the Lion asked.

"Yes, O Lion, it is," said the Rabbit. "I was asleep under a palm tree. I woke up and thought, 'What would become of me if the earth should all break up?' At that very moment, I heard the sound of the earth breaking up, and I ran away."

"Then," said the Lion, "you and I will go back to the place where the earth began to break up, and see what is the matter."

So the Lion put the little Rabbit on his back, and away they went like the wind. The other animals waited for them at the foot of the hill.

The Rabbit told the Lion when they were near the place where he slept, and the Lion saw just where the Rabbit had been sleeping.

He saw, too, the coconut that had fallen to the ground nearby. Then the Lion said to the Rabbit, "It must have been the sound of the coconut falling to the ground that you heard. You foolish Rabbit!"

And the Lion ran back to the other animals, and told them all about it.

If it had not been for the wise King of Beasts, they might be running still.

Conclusion:

These three selections are from *Jataka Tales*, retold by Ellen C. Babbitt, published by Appleton-Century-Crofts, Inc. There is a second volume entitled *More Jataka Tales*.

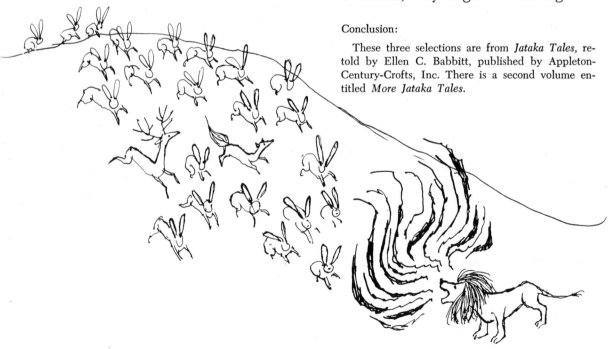

HIGH DIDDLE DIDDLE,
THE FOOL IN THE MIDDLE

The town of Gotham, in England, is famous for its merry men. Legend has it that Gotham was once known as Goats' Town, and that the inhabitants became playful tricksters in imitation of the goats. Many merry tales are told about the place, with Jack of Dover wandering through most of the stories and trying to decide whether the men of Gotham are really as foolish as they seem to be.

THERE WAS A MERRY MAN of Gotham a-riding on the road. His name was Brian, and though many called him silly, his life was full of laughter, which the many did not have. Merry Brian was sitting high on his bony piebald, and before him lay a yellow, bulging sack filled with two bushels of good wheat. He was riding to the market, full of joy at the money he would earn. To pass the time away he hummed a song:

> "Dibbity, dibbity, dibbity, doe
> Give me a pancake and I'll go.
> Dibbity, dibbity, dibbity, ditter,
> Please give me a bit of a fritter."

This was a little song sung by young folks on Shrove Tuesday in the still dusk to get a bit of pancake or a fritter. Merry Brian hummed the verse over and over, then he laughed loudly, remembering how the song had gained him many a good mouthful.

All of a sudden a crow, flashing blue-black in the sun, flew across his horse. That was an ill omen, so he cried:

"Crow, crow, get out of my sight,
Or I'll kill your father and mother tonight."

The crow flew off, crying *caw, caw,* and our merry man in green fustian was once again happy as the day.

Just as he was coming near Nottingham to Nottinghamshire Full of Hoggys, a tattered, steel-dark cloud passed across the sun, and the sun and the face of good Brian darkened.

"Alas," cried he, "I'm no better than a wild beast in the weird woods. Here I am sitting in great comfort atop o' my faithful horse that's labored for me many a year, and on top o' that I'm burdening the poor, kind beast, that has served me well, with two bushels of wheat on its back. Fie! I'm the cruelest carl in all of England."

Every moment he grew more angry at the thought.

"Shame upon me! Of what degree man am I to act so like a churl? I must have but half a heart."

167

He came to a brown wooden bridge spanning a little sparkling river, stopped the horse, and got down from it. Next he took off the sack full of wheat and put it across his own neck and tried to climb on the horse, but it was not easy. As luck would have it, Jack of Dover came by right then. Brian knew him well.

"Come, Jack," he cried, "help me mount my horse."

"Why don't you put the sack on the horse and then get up?" queried Jack.

"Because, friend Jack, I don't want to burden my good horse with the load of wheat. 'Tis sufficient that he carries me without complaint. I'll carry the wheat upon my back and save my good animal."

Jack looked and listened and did not know what to say. He was not certain whether Brian had played a game to fool him or was acting silly naturally. But he helped him get on the horse. Brian thanked him and went off with a light heart and a heavy burden on his neck.

"Friend," cried he to the horse, swallowing hard, "thus I reward you for your many years of service. By cock and fox, the burden is no longer upon your back but upon .my neck."

But Brian never felt the burden at all, for a good deed drives weight or worry away.

So he rode along in the sparkling sun, gay as any flashing bird in the air, while Jack of Dover still stood there like a plucked crow, greatly worried whether Brian was a fool or had done the silly thing just to fool him.

Now won't you sing with me:

High diddle diddle,
The fool in the middle.

Conclusion:

This is only one of many merry tales in the book *The Merry Men of Gotham*, by M. A. Jagendorf, published by Vanguard Press. You will also enjoy "Cuckoo in the Hedge" and "Rolling Cheese Gathers No Moss."

SOUP OF THE SOUP

Turkish boys and girls love to listen to the funny tales about Nasr-ed-Din Hodja. It is said that when Nasr-ed-Din was a boy, five centuries ago, he protested to his schoolmaster that he had not taken part in a prank played by his fellows, but had merely laughed at their mischief. The schoolmaster predicted that people would always laugh at Nasr-ed-Din, and so they do when stories are told about him.

"WHAT A FINE RABBIT!" Nasr-ed-Din Hodja smiled as he took the plump rabbit that Hussein, the villager, held out to him.

"I caught it especially for you!" Hussein's smile was as broad as the Hodja's own.

"Fatima! Fatima!" called Nasr-ed-Din Hodja.

Pulling the scarf over her face, Fa-

tima came bustling in from the kitchen.

"See what a feast Hussein has brought us!" The Hodja chuckled in anticipation of the good meal, as Fatima held out her hand for the limp rabbit. "I am asking him to stay and eat it with us. Cook it your very best!"

Left alone, the two men sat cross-legged on the floor and talked — at least, the Hodja talked and the villager listened. The Hodja knew it would be nearly two hours before the meal was ready, but what better way to pass two hours than to have a quiet listener? Nasr-ed-Din Hodja's voice droned on contentedly. There were stories of his childhood, of his school days, of his exploits at the court of Tamerlane the Great, of the everyday news of his own city of Ak Shehir. There were his views of this, and that, and the other. Hussein, the perfect listener, knew just when to shrug his shoulders, to click his tongue, to wag his head, to rub his hands together. The pungent fragrance of roasting rabbit floated about them.

At last the door opened and in scuffled the veiled Fatima with a huge tray of rabbit and pilaf and a big plate of thin bread. She set the food between the two men and went scurrying back to the part of the house where a woman belonged when there were guests. Breaking off bits of bread, the men curved them into spoons and scooped up great mouthfuls of the steaming pilaf and rabbit.

"What a cook!" sighed Hussein. There was just the right touch of garlic, just the right sprinkling of pistachio nuts, just the right dryness of rice.

"What a rabbit!" mumbled the Hodja, his mouth full to dripping.

They ate until their loose girdles were as tight as drumheads. They polished their plates with their bread to get the last succulent bit.

"There are still the bones left!" Nasr-ed-Din Hodja's voice was drowsy and contented. "Fatima's soups are as good as her pilafs."

Home to his village went Hussein, reporting to his neighbors how royally he had been treated at the home of Nasr-ed-Din Hodja.

The next morning, the Hodja was called to the door again. There stood two villagers — strangers. Remembering his treat of yesterday, the Hodja glanced quickly at their hands. Empty!

"What is your errand?" questioned the Hodja.

"We are the neighbors of the villager who brought you the rabbit yesterday." The men looked expectant. They seemed to be sniffing the air, which was already telling of the soup Fatima was preparing.

"Oh! A fine fellow is Hussein!" cried Nasr-ed-Din Hodja. *"Hosh geldinez —* your coming gives joy. Any neighbors of his are welcome. Come in! Come in! Dinner will soon be ready and you shall see what good soup Fatima can make of the bones of the rabbit. A great cook is my Fatima!"

Fatima, hearing the voices, padded softly into the room and peered through her veil. As she left the room, there were sounds behind her veil which might have meant, "What fun to have guests again." Or the sounds might have meant something very different.

Soon Fatima brought in a tray with three steaming bowls of soup, thick with rice and vegetables and tiny shreds of rabbit meat. She set the tray before the three men and slipped out of the room. The Hodja talked as he ate, but his stories did not flow with yesterday's enthusiasm.

The men thanked him for the meal and went back to their village, to tell of the hospitality of Nasr-ed-Din Hodja.

The next morning, the Hodja went warily to answer a knock at the door. There stood two other villagers — strangers again.

"And why am I honored with this call?" Nasr-ed-Din Hodja had already glanced at their hands and found them dangling empty at their sides.

"We are the neighbors of the neighbors of the villager who brought you the rabbit." The two men grinned hopefully.

Nasr-ed-Din Hodja blinked, then said, "Come in and share my humble meal."

The men walked in and squatted on the floor while the Hodja went into the kitchen. He poured a kettle of hot water over the spoonful that remained of yesterday's soup. He poured the liquid into bowls which he carried to the room where the men were waiting.

"Oh, neighbors of the neighbors of

the villager who brought me the delicious rabbit!" Nasr-ed-Din Hodja's cordiality was loud. "May you enjoy this soup of the soup of the bones of the rabbit."

One neighbor of the neighbors of Hussein looked at his bowl of water in which two grains of rice swam beside a scrap of turnip. The other neighbor of the neighbors of Hussein looked at his bowl of water in which two grains of rice swam with a shred of onion and a chip of carrot. Nasr-ed-Din Hodja made a great noise of emptying his bowl before he smiled his guests to the door.

And the next day Fatima and Nasr-

ed-Din Hodja sat down to a quiet meal together once more.

Conclusion:

This story is taken from *Once the Hodja*, by Alice Geer Kelsey, published by Longmans, Green & Co. Other funny stories in this book are "Pumpkin Trees and Walnut Vines" and "The Bear in the Pear Tree."

THE WONDERFUL KNAPSACK

Very popular in Denmark, this folk tale appeals to boys and girls everywhere. It appears in different versions in the folk literature of several countries.

ONCE UPON A TIME there was a soldier who had served his king well for ten years and a day, but alas, alack, when he came to get his pay for all the wars he had won, the king was as poor as he, and there were only three pennies left in the royal treasury.

"Well," said the soldier, "I'll not worry about it. I'll take my pay in honor and glory."

"To be sure," said the king, "honor and glory are all very well, but they'll not keep the wolf from the door. I will give you the palace plates. They are pure gold and will sell for a high price."

"Then you could not eat like a king," cried the soldier, "and that would never do. No indeed, your majesty, give me the three pennies and I will be on my way."

"Very well, then," said the king, and he scooped up the three lone pennies from the bottom of the royal treasury and laid them in the hand of the soldier. "May they bring you luck," he said, and the soldier thanked him and went whistling on his way.

Now, when he had walked a mile or so, whom should he meet but an old, old crone, bent in the middle and with scarcely a tooth in her head.

"A penny from the young for the old," begged the old woman.

"A penny!" exclaimed the soldier. "Why, I've but three pennies in the whole, wide world. Still, it little matters if there are three or two," and so he gave the old woman one of the pennies.

Then he walked on another mile or so, till what should he come upon but a second old crone more bent and toothless than the first!

"A penny from the young for the old," begged the old woman.

"A penny!" cried the soldier. "Why, all I have in the whole, wide world is two pennies. Still, it little matters if there's two or one," and he gave the old woman the second of the pennies.

Then he walked on with the one lone penny, till after a mile or so he was stopped by a third old crone so bent that her chin almost touched her knees.

"A penny from the young for the old," said this old creature, and the soldier exclaimed, "One penny is all I have in the world. But it little matters if I've one or none," and he gave the last penny to the old woman.

At this, the old creature changed into a young and beautiful girl, for she was not really an old crone at all, but a fairy who had tested the soldier three times to see if he were good and brave.

"What a kind and generous lad you are," exclaimed the fairy. "And for that you deserve to be generously rewarded. I will give you three wishes, and all of them will come true."

But what do you know, the soldier could not think of a thing to wish for! He had two strong arms, two long legs, and a head set straight on his shoulders,

172

and that was all he had ever wanted. At length, however, he said, "I wish to have a long life and a healthy one."

"You have wished a good wish," said the fairy. "Now for your other wishes."

Now the soldier had a knapsack that had been with him in the wars, and he liked the fit and the feel of it, particularly when it was full, so at last he said, "I wish that my knapsack will never wear out. And I wish last, that whatever I want will go into my knapsack, and whatever I want will come out."

"Three better wishes were never made," said the fairy, "nor three more easily granted. Now good-bye, and good luck." And with that the fairy disappeared, and the soldier went happily on his way.

Toward evening he reached the town, and as he was very hungry, in he walked to the best inn and sat down at the finest table. "Landlord," he called, "serve me food, and serve it well," and the landlord came running.

But when the landlord saw a torn and tattered soldier instead of a silk and satin lord, he cried, "We will feed you food aplenty, good soldier, but you must come into the kitchen."

"No, thank you," said the soldier. "This will do quite nicely, I am sure. Of course, I am used to finer linen and brighter candlelight, but as I am hungry, it will not matter. Now bring me two bottles of your best wine and a dozen chicken breasts and be quick about it."

At this bold talk, the landlord quickly changed his tune, for of course, no plain, ordinary soldier would speak in such a fashion, and this one must surely be a prince in disguise.

"Yes, sir, whatever you wish, sir," he said politely, and then he ran to set the table with his finest linen and dishes and to serve the food just as the soldier had ordered.

When all was ready, the soldier fell to eating at once, for he was quite famished, but near the end, he remembered to leave a good bit on his plate, since that, of course, is always what lords and ladies do. Then he wished a handful of gold coins into the knapsack, and taking out two of them, tossed them to the landlord.

"I trust this will pay for the meal," he said.

"It is payment, and more," said the landlord, and he bowed so low he bumped his head on the floor. "I hope

everything suited your taste, your excellency."

"Fairly well, my good man," said the soldier. "Now you must provide me with a room for the night."

But alas, there were no rooms — and the landlord almost wept to say this — there were no rooms save one, and that could not be used.

"And why not?" exclaimed the soldier.

"Who goes in there alive comes out dead," cried the landlord.

"Is that all?" laughed the soldier. "Then that is the very room for me. Sweep it clean and make the bed well, for I am tired tonight."

The landlord wrung his hands, and the maids cried, and all the rich diners shook their heads, but nothing would do but that the soldier sleep in the dreadful room; and so it was prepared, and when the soldier had smoked awhile by the fire and felt a little drowsy, he bid everyone good night and went up to it.

Inside, he locked the door, stood his faithful knapsack in a corner where he could keep his eye on it, and sat down in a chair to see what would happen.

He had only a moment to wait until there was a great rustling in the chimney and a black ball came rolling out

of the fireplace and into the center of the room. There it unrolled itself, and the soldier saw the ugliest troll ever seen in the whole, wide world, with eyes red as fire and fingers like claws. Then out rolled a second troll, and after that a third, each uglier than the other, and both much worse than the first.

"How do you do?" said the soldier. "How very nice of you to come and keep me company! Now do sit down and make yourselves at home," and he pointed to three chairs on the other side of the fireplace.

The three trolls seated themselves, but not for long. In a minute they were up and at the soldier. One tweaked his nose, the other pulled his ears, and the third one tried to pin down his arms.

"Dear me," said the soldier, "I must say this is a strange way for guests to act. Well, if you can do no better, into my knapsack you must go." And there and then, into the knapsack they had to creep, and soon only a creaking and hissing could be heard.

"I hope you are comfortable there," said the soldier. "But if you are not, 'tis your own fault, to be sure. And now you must answer me a question. Why do you pester this room every night?"

There was a great silence for a moment, but whether they would or nay, the trolls had to give up their secret.

"We guard the oven," said the first.

"To protect the treasure," said the second.

"And woe to him who tries to steal it," said the third.

"Very well," said the soldier. "And thank you for the information." Then

174

he undressed, for he was very tired, and went straight to bed.

Next morning the landlord, and the maids, and all the rich diners came to see what had happened to the remarkable soldier. They knocked on the door and peeked through the keyhole, but as the soldier was still sleeping he did not hear them, and so they thought he was dead and set up a great weeping and wailing.

"He was so young and handsome," cried all the maids.

"He was so rich," cried the landlord.

"And he ate like a prince," cried all the rich diners.

Now all this fuss and bother finally awakened the soldier, and he cried out crossly, "Landlord, landlord, what's all this fuss?"

"Oh, my!" cried everyone. "You're not still alive, are you?"

"Alive and ready to eat," answered the soldier. "Landlord, serve me a dozen fresh eggs and a pail of warm milk."

This the landlord ran to do, followed by the maids and diners, and when all was ready, the soldier got up and dressed, took a good look at his knapsack, then locked his room and went down to eat.

And when he had eaten, he commanded the landlord to bring him three strong men. "They must take my knapsack to the blacksmith's and beat the dust out of it," said the soldier. "I have walked a long mile or two in my day, and the knapsack is powerfully dusty."

The landlord did as he was ordered, though truth to tell, he considered it quite a strange request, and soon three strong men were lugging and tugging at the knapsack which looked light as a feather but weighed heavy as lead. And when they reached the blacksmith's shop, they were so tired they could hardly lift a finger, to say nothing of wielding a heavy hammer, so three of the blacksmith's strongest helpers were set to the task of beating the knapsack.

But what a shrieking was heard when they started their work, shrieking enough to set your hair on end!

175

"Don't mind a little noise," said the soldier. "My knapsack is squeaky at the seams. Just beat as hard as you can."

So the men went on, and after a while, all was quiet. Then the soldier said, "There, that's clean enough. Now be so good as to empty it into the sea."

But these poor fellows were now so tired they could scarce lift a finger, to say nothing of carrying a heavy knapsack down to the sea, so three more huskies were found, and they lugged and tugged till the strange knapsack was down to the shore. Then they opened it, and what a pile of black dust poured into the water! It was all that was left of the three dreadful trolls, and good riddance, too, though it blackened the sea for a mile around.

The workmen were now paid for their hard labor, and generously, too, with a handful of gold for each of them, and then the soldier returned to the landlord.

"Landlord," he cried, "I have one last task for you. In the room where I slept last night, there stands a big oven, and this you must tear down at once."

"Well," said the landlord to himself, "he'll soon want to pull down the roof from over my head, but I'll not question money." So he did as the soldier commanded, and there under the oven, what should he find but a pot of gold as big as a washtub!

"What a clever fellow you were to discover all this gold," exclaimed the landlord.

"Oh, 'twas nothing at all," said the soldier. "Now take it, good landlord, all of it, and use it well." Then he took up his knapsack and bid his host good-bye. But the landlord would not let him go without half the money, and this he could not refuse. But it was a heavy load to carry, and so he must stay a bit longer. And then whom should he meet but the landlord's daughter, a very pretty lass, and so he must tarry still longer, till the lass was his bride, and then — well, with health, wealth, and happiness, he no doubt tarries there still.

Conclusion:

Mary C. Hatch collected this and other stories in *13 Danish Tales*, published by Harcourt, Brace and Company. You will also enjoy "The Talking Pot" and "Peter Humbug and the White Cat" from the same book.

176

A CLEVER JUDGE

The people who tell this tale live on the vast steppes or prairies of southwestern Asia. They are herders of cattle, sheep, and goats. And they are clever fellows, too, as you shall see.

THERE LIVED A MAN in the steppes who was famous for his justice and wisdom. At that time if a man was known for his fairness, people came to him from far and wide to ask him to settle their disputes. And so it was that one day two villagers appeared before this wise man and asked him to settle their quarrel.

"Tell me your story," the judge said to the plaintiff.

"I had to leave my village," said the plaintiff, "for I had business elsewhere. And all my wealth was a hundred gold coins. I did not come by them easily. I had to work hard for them, and I did not want them to be stolen while I was away. Nor did I care to carry so much money with me on my journey. So I entrusted these gold coins for safe-

keeping to this man here. When I got back from my journey, he denied that he had ever received the money from me."

"And who saw you give him these hundred gold coins?" asked the judge.

"No one saw it. We went together to the heart of the forest and there I handed him the coins."

"What have you to say to this?" the judge asked, turning to the defendant.

The defendant shrugged his shoulders.

"I don't know what he is talking about," said the man. "I never went to the forest with him. I never saw his gold coins."

"Do you remember the place where you handed over the money?" the judge asked the plaintiff.

"Of course I do. It was under a tall oak. I remember it very well. I can point it out with no trouble at all."

"So you do have a witness, after all," said the judge. "Here, take my signet ring, go to the tall tree under which you stood when you handed over the money, set the seal of my signet ring against the trunk, and bid the tree appear before me to bear out the truth of your story."

The plaintiff took the signet ring and went off to carry out the demand of the judge. The defendant remained behind and waited for his return.

After some time had passed, the judge turned to the defendant and asked, "Do you think he has reached the oak by this time?"

"No, not yet," was the answer.

After further time had passed, the judge again turned to the defendant and asked, "Do you think he has reached the tree by this time?"

"Yes," was the answer, "by now he must have reached it."

Not long after that the plaintiff returned.

"Well?" asked the judge.

"I did just as you said," replied the plaintiff. "I walked as far as the forest and then I went on until I came to the tall oak under which we stood when I handed over my gold coins. I set the seal of your signet ring against the trunk of the tree and I bade it appear before you as a witness. But the tree refused to budge."

"Never mind," said the judge. "The oak has appeared before me and it has borne witness in your favor."

At that the defendant exclaimed, "How can you say such a thing! I have been here all this while and no tree has stalked into the place."

"But," replied the judge, "you said that you had not been in the forest at all. And yet when I asked you whether the plaintiff had reached the oak, first you answered that he could not have reached it, and the second time you said that he must surely have reached it. Therefore, you *were* in the forest and you remembered where the oak was under which you stood when the plaintiff handed his gold coins to you for safekeeping. Now you must not only return him his hundred gold pieces, but you must also pay a fine for having tried to cheat him."

So the tree was a witness without budging, and justice was done.

Conclusion:

This story is taken from *Tales of Faraway Folk,* chosen and retold by Babette Deutsch and Avrahm Yarmolinsky, and published by Harper & Brothers. Among the others included are "The One Who Wasn't Afraid" and "The Owl's Punishment."

THE TWO STONE GIANTS

Frances Carpenter has gathered Korean folk tales from many sources and adapted them for American boys and girls. She has created the fictional household of Kim, in which Halmoni the grandmother retells the tales for the others, and particularly for the children Ok Cha and Yong Tu.

DOG WAS BARKING, and servants were rushing this way and that in the Outer Court. Old Pak had run to open the bamboo gate, and Yong Tu and his cousins raced around the corner of the Hall of Perfect Learning. The Master of the House was returning from his journey to Songdo, the old High Tree Capital, far to the north. His traveling chair was already in sight down the street.

The sedan chair bearers in their blue suits and red sashes trotted in through the bamboo gate. They seemed as fresh as if they had not borne their master many miles over the rough Korean

country roads. Kim Hong Chip rose from his seat on the floor of the little curtained box which they had set down on the ground. He stepped stiffly out between the poles on which it was slung and walked across the hard-packed earth of the courtyard. Even with changing his position again and again, and with descending from the chair to walk over smooth level parts of the roads, his legs were cramped with his long journey.

"Bring the package to the Inner Court," Kim Hong Chip said to a servant. Then, followed by the children, he made his way to Halmoni's apartment to report his safe return.

The old woman's eyes sparkled with pleasure when the package disclosed two beautiful bowls of clear, sea-green porcelain. Songdo, once the capital and the center of Korean art, was famous for such delicate vases with their patterns wrought clearly under the gleaming green surface.

All the family gathered about the Master of the House when he had finished his evening meal. He was tired, and his wife had brought his eating table to him in Halmoni's room. No one spoke while the Master was dining, for in Korea then it was thought that talk

along the way to frighten off the bad spirits. We took care to toss stones on the spirit piles under the trees. And I got down out of my chair to bow before the two great *miryeks*. These men of stone are very big, Omoni. They look very powerful. Bad spirits surely must fear them."

The man was speaking of two giant stone figures along the travel route between Korea's capital city, Seoul, and its former old High Tree Capital, Songdo. All through this land there are stone figures like these, which the people called *miryeks,* or men of stone. Smaller ones are the devil posts, set up to protect villages and roads from bad spirits which might be riding by on the winds. Others are great giants in stone, carved on the faces of the cliffs or out of some rocky point.

"Were those two *miryeks* as big as the White Buddha, Abuji?" Yong Tu asked his father. The boy once made a picnic journey with his family to see this Great White Buddha which is carved on a cliff a few miles from their city of Seoul. A stream ran at its foot. The country folk in the valley there say that no matter how great the floods are, water never touches the garments of this likeness of the wise teacher, Buddha. A little roof over its towering

spoiled the food. "Eat while you eat, and talk when you have finished," Halmoni taught her grandchildren.

"Tell us of your journey, great traveler," the old woman said when the brass rice spoon had been laid down and the chopsticks had been wiped clean of *kimchee* and put into their embroidered case.

"It was a good journey, and luck traveled with me," Kim Hong Chip began. "There were demon posts often

head keeps the rain and the sleet from washing the statue's white paint away too quickly.

"*Yé*, my son, these two *miryeks* are even taller than the White Buddha. Like a giant man and his wife, they stand side by side. A man and a woman they are, too, carved from great pointed rocks."

"There's a story about those two *miryeks*," Halmoni said, thoughtfully. "They were built to drive away beggars, not spirits, so my grandmother said. And they did drive the beggars away, but not as their builder had planned."

"Now I recall that tale, too, Omoni," the old woman's son said. "Tell it to the children, as you told it to me when I was the age of Yong Tu."

"Well, those *miryeks* are not far from the place where a rich man once lived. He had a fine house with five different gates. I do not remember his name, but we may as well call him Yong. Yong's heart was kind, like that of Yo in the story of the Magic Cat. Like Woo, the Spoonmaker, he never could bring himself to turn beggars away from his gate.

"In processions the beggars came. Buddhist priests with their begging bowls and little brass bells; poor farmers whose rice plants had yielded no grain that year; even city folk from whom wicked officials had taken their last strings of *cash* — all these trod the well-worn path to Yong's open gates. The servants in that household were kept running back and forth from morning till night to put rice and *cash* into the outstretched hands of those beggars.

"But when water is always poured out of a bowl and none is poured in, the bowl soon is empty, my little dragons. So it was with Yong's *cash* chests. He became frightened at the lessening number of the coins on their bottoms.

"One afternoon a traveler knocked at the gate and asked if he might come in for a rest. This one was an old man, and he wore a poet's hat. Yong invited the

aged scholar into his House of Guests. He offered him a bowl of hot rice and a cup of good wine to refresh him.

" 'Wisdom drips from your tongue, honorable sir,' Yong said to his visitor. 'Give me of your jade counsel. So many *cash* have I given away to the beggars who crowd my gate that my fortune soon will be gone. Yet I cannot bring myself to turn them away. What can I do?'

"The old man sat quiet, thinking. Then he spoke thus, 'It is very simple. If the Great Man will come out with me into the courtyard, I will show him the way.' There he pointed to two tall pillars of stone which jutted out of a cliff not far away. 'Make those rocks into *miryeks*. Carve them into a giant man and a giant woman. When the great stone figures are completed, I promise you no more beggars will come to your gate.'

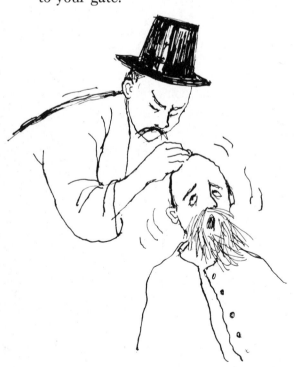

"When the old man had departed, Yong thought long over his words, 'Making *miryeks* would cost too much,' he said at first. But so many more beggars clamored for *cash* that he decided to follow the old man's advice.

"And the stone carving did cost much. It cost all the *cash* in all the rich man's money boxes. But finally the two giant *miryeks* stood there, as tall and as powerful as they look today. Each wore a stone hat on its head and stone robes on its shoulders.

"Not long thereafter the learned old traveler again called at Yong's gate. But Yong had no pleasant, polite words of welcome for him this time. He grabbed him by his gray topknot, and he shook him well. 'How dare you come back here again, Old Man?' he cried. 'You have brought ruin upon me, you and your *miryeks!*'

"But the old man only smiled and asked, 'Will the Great Man be pleased to have a little patience? What was the charm you asked of me?'

" 'I asked for a charm to keep beggars away.'

" 'And does this charm not work? I saw no beggars at your gate.'

"Yong looked crestfallen. 'No, there are no beggars there,' he admitted. 'They well know there is nothing here for them now.'

" 'Then you should not complain. I gave you the charm for which you asked. And you have learned what everyone else in this land knows — the only place where beggars are not is where there is nothing to be given away.'

"Yong bowed to the old man, begging his pardon. 'You speak wise words again,' he said. 'It is I who have been foolish. But it would have been better for me to empty my money chests for poor hungry beggars rather than for those two people of stone.'"

Conclusion:

Halmoni tells many more ancient stories in the book *Tales of a Korean Grandmother*, by Frances Carpenter, published by Doubleday & Company, Inc. Other favorites are "Why the Dog and the Cat Are Not Friends" and "The Man Who Lived a Thousand Years."

JOKES

MOTHER: "Did you thank Mrs. Porter for the lovely party she gave?"
LITTLE DOROTHY: "No, Mommie, I didn't. The girl leaving just before me thanked her and Mrs. Porter said, 'Don't mention it,' so I didn't."

BIG SISTER: "Bobby, if you eat the rest of that pumpkin pie, you'll burst!"
BOBBY: "Okay. Pass the pie and get outa the way."

RUSTY: "So you missed your train?"
BUSTER: "Yes!"
RUSTY: "By how much did you miss it?"
BUSTER: "I missed it by just a minute."
RUSTY: "Well, don't get so excited. The way you're carrying on, it's as if you missed it by an hour."

FARMER: "What are you doing up in that tree, young fellow?"
BOY: "One of your apples fell down, and I'm trying to put it back!"

PAPA KANGAROO: "Anabelle, where's the baby?"
MAMA KANGAROO: "My goodness! I've had my pocket picked!"

The absent-minded professor staggered from a train, his complexion very white.

"Riding backwards for ten hours," he explained. "I never could stand that."

"Why," his wife inquired, "didn't you ask the person sitting opposite to change seats with you?"

"I couldn't do that," said the professor. "There wasn't anybody there."

TEACHER: "Randy, if you put your hand in one pants pocket and you find seventy-five cents and you put your hand in the other pants pocket and you find twenty-five cents, what would you have?"
RANDY, promptly: "I'd have somebody else's pants on!"

NEIGHBOR: "I understand your son is on the football team. What does he play?"
MOTHER: "I think he's one of the drawbacks."

SHOPPER: "How much are these tomatoes?"
GROCER: "Forty cents a pound."
SHOPPER: "Did you raise them yourself?"
GROCER: "Yes, ma'am, I certainly did. They were only thirty-five cents yesterday."

EDYTH: "She said your hair was dyed."
REDYTH: "It's false!"
EDYTH: "That's what *I* told her."

Little Betty was crying bitterly. Teacher asked what was the matter.

"Oooh! My new shoes *hurt* me!" said Betty.

"Well, no wonder," explained Teacher, "you have them on the wrong feet."

But Betty kept right on crying. "*haven't* any other feet!" she cried.

POP PARKER, to a friend at work: "Well, we've managed to furnish three of the rooms in our house with the soap coupons my wife collects."
FRIEND: "Furnished three rooms by collecting soap coupons? Aren't you going to furnish the other three rooms?"
POP PARKER: "No — they're full of soap."

BERNIE: "We've got a hen down at our house that lays white eggs."
ERNIE: "What's so wonderful about that?"
BERNIE: "Can *you* do it?"

DOPEY: "My grampa made a scarecrow so terrible that it frightened every single crow off the place."
DOPIER: "You think *that's* something? I made one that scared 'em so much they brought back the corn they stole last year!"

LOUIE: "How did you like the play last night?"
HUGHIE: "I saw the first act, but not the second."
LOUIE: "Why not?"
HUGHIE: "I couldn't wait that long. It said on the program — second act, two years later."

POLLY: "How did Santa Claus treat you?"
MOLLY: "He brought me this lovely woolen sweater."
POLLY: "That isn't wool. It's plainly marked 'cotton.'"
MOLLY: "Yes, I know — that's to fool the moths."

The farmer watched the paratroop maneuvers with evident interest. Finally, one of the paratroopers landed in a tree nearby. The farmer watched the soldier as he cut himself away from his harness and scrambled down.

"Boy," said the G.I., "that was something."

"Sure was," drawled the farmer. "First time I ever did see a man climb down a tree without climbing up first."

SAMMY: "Do you think anyone can predict the future with cards?"
DANNY: "My mother can. She takes one look at my report cards, then tells me exactly what will happen when my dad gets home."

MRS. PRETTY: "Whenever I'm in the dumps, I get a new hat."
MRS. MEAN: "Oh, so *that's* where you get them!"

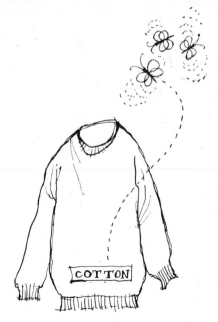

185

CITY MORON: "Why does cream cost more than milk?"
COUNTRY MORON: "Because it's harder for the cows to sit on the small bottles."

"What do you believe is the reason for your long life, Uncle Ebenezer?" asked the reporter on Uncle Ebenezer's one-hundred-and-second birthday.

Uncle Ebenezer thought for a moment or two, then, "Well, I guess it's because I was born a long time back, I guess," he said reflectively.

"Freddie," said his mother. "I wish you would run down the street and see how old Mrs. Cheever is this morning."

"Okay," Freddie agreed, and soon he returned and reported.

"Mrs. Cheever said it's none of your business how old she is."

GEORGIE: "Teacher, would you scold anybody for something they didn't do?"
TEACHER: "Of course not. But why, Georgie?"
GEORGIE: "Well, I didn't do my arithmetic!"

ARITHMETIC TEACHER: "If I gave you two apples and told you to give one to your brother, would you give him the little one or the big one?"
GEORGIE: "Do you mean my *little* brother, or my *big* brother?"

SALESMAN: "Sonny, is your mother at home?"
LITTLE SAMMY: "Yes, sir."
SALESMAN: (after knocking for some time and getting no answer): "I thought you said she was at home?"
LITTLE SAMMY: "Yes, sir, but I don't live here."

TEACHER (answering the phone): "You say George Gage has a bad cold and can't come to school? Who is this speaking?"
VOICE (with assumed hoarseness): "This is my father."

MOTHER: "Now Eddie, you must not be selfish. You must let your little brother have the sled half the time."
EDDIE: "But Mother, I do. I have it going down the hill, and *he* has it coming up."

BIG BROTHER: "Well, Joe, how do you like school?"
JOE: "Closed!"

JACK: "Today I saw a baby that gained ten pounds in two weeks by drinking elephant's milk."
MARY: "You don't say! Whose baby was it?"
JACK: "The elephant's."

The embarrassed city hostess said to her country cousin: "I thought I suggested you come after supper."

"Right," said the country cousin, "that *is* what I came after."

DOOPEY: "I hope the rain keeps up."
LOOPEY: "Why?"
DOOPEY: "So it won't come down."

Conclusion:

The above jokes, and hundreds of others just as good, are to be found in the book *Jokes, Jokes, Jokes,* edited by Helen Hoke, and published by Franklin Watts, Inc.

BRAIN TEASERS

I KNOW HOW MANY ARE IN YOUR FAMILY

Multiply the number of brothers you have by 2. Add 3 and multiply by 5. Add the number of your sisters and multiply by 10. Add the number of others in your family. What is your answer? (Subtract 150 from the answer. Then the last figure on the right is the number of "others" in your family; the next figure to the left is the number of sisters, and the next figure after that, to the left, is the number of brothers.) Here's how it works:

Multiply number of brothers
  (say 0) by 2   0
Add 3   3
Multiply by 5   15
Add the number of your sisters
  (say 2)   17

Multiply by 10   170
Add the number of others in
  your family (say 2)   172
Subtract 150 from your answer 022
So you have 0 brothers, 2 sisters and 2 others in your family.

MAGIC NUMBER 15873

The number 15873 behaves mysteriously when you multiply it by 7, and then by 14, 21, 28, and so on in multiples of 7. Try it and see.

HOW OLD ARE YOU?

Multiply your age by 3. Add 6, then divide by 3. What is your answer? (I can then tell you your age by subtracting 2 from your answer.) Here's how it works. Suppose you are 15 years old:

Multiply by 3	45
Add 6	51
Divide by 3	17
Subtract 2 from your answer	15

Try it with any age.

ALWAYS FIVE

Choose any number, say 111	111
Add 7	118
Multiply by 2	236
Subtract 4	232
Divide by 2	116
Subtract your chosen number	111

Your answer is always 5.

THE THREE FARMERS

On returning from the dairy, three co-operative farmers have 7 full pails of milk left and 7 pails half full. They also have 7 empty pails. How can they divide what is left (without pouring milk from one pail to another) so that each farmer gets the same amount of milk and the same number of pails to take home?

Full pails, half-full pails and empty pails can be divided 2-3-2, 2-3-2 and 3-1-3; or 3-1-3, 3-1-3 and 1-5-1.

OLDER OR YOUNGER?

Tom is three years younger than Tim. Toby is two years older than Tom. Is Tim older or younger than Toby? How many years?

Tim is one year older.

THE THREE CANDIDATE DETECTIVES

A chief of detectives had three likely candidates for an opening in his department. To test their powers of reasoning he told them: "I am going to make either a red or black mark on the forehead of each of you. At least one of the marks will be black. Without any help other than your own reasoning, I want you to determine the color of the mark on your own forehead. The first to do this and give me a satisfactory explanation of how you arrived at a conclusion will get the job."

He then blindfolded the men. Taking an inkpad from his drawer, he pressed one of his fingers on it and placed a black mark on the forehead of each man. He then carefully washed his hands and removed all traces of the color used. Finally he removed the blindfolds.

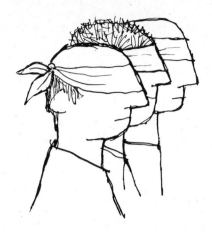

The three candidates looked at one another for several minutes. Each could see that the other two had black marks, but since only one of the marks must be black, he would have to assume at first that his own mark might be either red or black. However, one of the candidates finally said, "I have a black mark on my forehead." How did he come to this decision?

The Three Candidate Detectives. The winning candidate — call him A — reasoned as follows: "If I have a red mark on my forehead, B would quickly decide that he has a black mark by this line of thought: 'A's mark is red; if mine were red, C could instantly decide that his is black since at least one mark must be black; therefore, mine must be black.' C could come to the same conclusion as B. But since neither of these smart men has reached this rather obvious conclusion, the situation must be confused by the fact that there is a black mark on my forehead also."

TWO PINTS OF WATER

You have a gallon pail full of water. You also have a five-pint can and a three-pint can, both empty, and no other measuring cup. With only these containers, can you measure out exactly one pint of water into each of the cans?

(1) Fill the 5-pint can from the pail.
(2) Fill the 3-pint can from the five-pint can.
(3) Empty the 3-pint can into the pail.
(4) Pour the 2 pints left in the 5-pint can into the 3-pint can.
(5) Fill the 5-pint can from the pail (leaving 1 pint in the pail).
(6) To the 2 pints in the 3-pint can, add 1 pint from the 5-pint can.
(7) Pour the contents of the 3-pint can down the drain.
(8) Fill the 3-pint can again from the 5-pint can, leaving 1 pint in the latter.
(9) Empty the 3-pint can again and pour into it the 1 pint left in the pail.

NOT HIS MOTHER!

A boy entered the kitchen where his mother was working and said: "I am your son, but you are not my mother." How could this be possible?

Not His Mother! The boy was speaking to his father who was also in the kitchen.

NO CHANGE

A man has $1.15, all in regular United States coins. But even with this much money he cannot make change for a nickel, a dime, a quarter, a half dollar or a dollar. None of his coins is a silver dollar. What coins has he?

A half-dollar, a quarter and 4 dimes.

JIMMY'S MONEY

Jimmy spent one-fourth of his money at the store. On the way home he lost three-fourths of what he had left. When he got home he still had 9 cents. How much money did he have before he went to the store?

48 cents.

HIDDEN ANIMALS

Find the name of a familiar animal hidden in each of these sentences. For instance, in the first sentence start with the letter "r" in crab and see what you find.

1. A crab bit my finger.
2. An hour ago a truck passed heading south.
3. My cousin Alec owns a tractor.
4. On this trail I once saw a real Indian.
5. Susie and Bob earned the money for their trip.
6. Please wipe this dish or set it aside.
7. A missionary tries to help ignorant savages.
8. Everyone came late for my party.
9. We reached London keyed with excitement.
10. Fran's teeth are certainly clean and bright.

Hidden Animals

1. rabbit	6. horse
2. goat	7. pig
3. cow	8. camel
4. lion	9. donkey
5. bear	10. hare

SECRET CODES

Soldiers, you know, often send their messages in code. They don't want the enemy to be able to read what they write. Some codes are very hard to "break," but you can have fun finding out what the coded words below mean.

In these lists of familiar things, each letter stands for some other letter. Look at the first word under Pets. The first, third, and fourth letters of this five-letter word are all the same. Can you think of a kind of pet spelled that way? Think of some pets and soon you will come to PUPPY. That fits all right, doesn't it? Now you know that in all of the words of this puzzle, B is P, H is U,

GIANT BHBBU

190

and U is Y. So the second pet should be spelled __ U P P __ __ __. What might that be? When you think of it, you will know a few more letters of the code. You don't have to decode the words in order if you don't want to. Find one that seems easy to you and start from there.

PETS

B H B B U	Q X C R S P O
I H B B Z P R	S H O S F P
I Y F G V Z R Q	T X A X O U
W Z S S P A	T Q Z T W

Secret Codes
Pets: PUPPY, GUPPIES, GOLDFISH, KITTEN, HAMSTER, TURTLE, CANARY, CHICK.

GUESS WHAT I AM

My first letter is in take, but not in give.
My second is in die, and also in live.
My third is in go, but not in stop.
My fourth is in raise, but not in drop.
My last is in where, but not in who.
My whole is a beast you see in the zoo.

My first is in even, but not in odd.
My second is in scepter, but not in rod.
My third is in long, but not in short.
My fourth is in hunt, but not in sport.
My last is in waist, but not in girth.
My whole is a close neighbor of the
  earth.

My first is in cave, but not in rock.
My second is in latch, but not in lock.
My third is in pain, but not in hurt.
My fourth is in cute, but not in pert.
My fifth is in poem, but not in verse.
My sixth is in curt, but not in terse.

My seventh is in dive, but not in swim.
My eighth is in edge, but not in rim.
My last is in spirit, but not in ghost.
My whole is a port on Canada's west
  coast.

Guess What I Am: Tiger. Venus. Vancouver.

TOOLS OF SPORTS

Each of the following is a piece of equipment used in a particular sport. Identify each with its sport.

1. Puck	_____	Badminton
2. Niblick	_____	Fencing
3. Jack	_____	Ice hockey
4. Pelota	_____	Curling
5. Wicket	_____	Billiards
6. Stone	_____	Cricket
7. Shuttlecock	_____	Lawn bowling
8. Foil	_____	Fishing
9. Reel	_____	Jai alai
10. Cue	_____	Golf

191

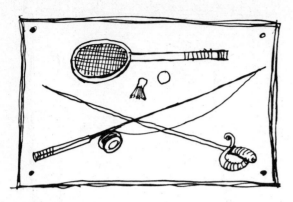

AGES

Each of the words defined below ends in *-age*. When you have guessed all of the words correctly, the column of first letters in each of these puzzles will spell out the name of a famous Greek scholar and teacher.

What is good to eat?
What is the age of being too old?
What age is good for tying things?
What is the age of great fury?
What age is something attached?
What is the age of cultivating land?
What is the age to join battle?
What age is fodder for livestock?

What age is to soothe or relieve?
What age is to search thoroughly?
What age is a likeness?
What age is a platform?
What age is teaching?
What is the age of resistance of an electrical conductor?
What age is the act of pulling a barge?

What age is the escape of a fluid?
What is the age to stir up anger?

What is the age of bestowing favors?
What age is tied together in a chain?
What age is a natural inheritance?
What age is the cost of hauling goods?
What age is a home for parentless children?

Ages:

Sausage	Assuage	Patronage
Overage	Rummage	Linkage
Cordage	Image	Appanage
Rage	Stage	Truckage
Appendage	Tutelage	Orphanage
Tillage	Ohmage	
Engage	Towage	
Silage	Leakage	
	Enrage	

WHAT SCIENTISTS DO

Each of these kinds of scientists is mainly interested in one of the things in the right-hand column. Match the scientist with the subject of his work.

192

1. Entomologist — Diseases
2. Philologist — Fossils
3. Agronomist — Races of man
4. Paleontologist — The universe
5. Ichthyologist — Insects
6. Psychologist — Rocks
7. Ethnologist — Human institutions
8. Physiologist — Ancient ruins
9. Meteorologist — Language
10. Sociologist — Surface of the earth
11. Pathologist — Use of the land
12. Petrologist — Functions of living organs
13. Archaeologist — Fishes
14. Physiographer — The mind
15. Cosmographer — Air and weather

Answers:

1. Insects. 2. Language. 3. Use of the land. 4. Fossils. 5. Fishes. 6. The mind. 7. Races of man. 8. Functions of living organs. 9. Air and weather. 10. Human institutions. 11. Diseases. 12. Rocks. 13. Ancient ruins. 14. Surface of the earth. 15. The universe.

GREAT DISCOVERIES AND INVENTIONS

Match each of the following with its discoverer or inventor.

1. Antiseptic surgery — George Westinghouse
2. Glider — Evangelista Torricelli
3. Sewing machine — R. H. Goddard
4. Vaccination — Jonas E. Salk
5. Liquid-fuel rocket — E. Cartwright
6. Anesthetics — Joseph Lister
7. Air brake — James Stephenson
8. Dynamo — Otto Lilienthal
9. Polio vaccine — Sir Humphrey Davy
10. Locomotive — Elias Howe
11. Barometer — Michael Faraday
12. Power loom — Edward Jenner

Answers:

1. Lister. 2. Lilienthal. 3. Howe. 4. Jenner. 5. Goddard. 6. Davy. 7. Westinghouse. 8. Faraday. 9. Salk. 10. Stephenson. 11. Torricelli. 12. Cartwright.

RHYMING CLICHÉS

As you read off each of the trite sayings in the left-hand column, the players are to write down another that rhymes with the one you give. Some possible answers are given in the right-hand column.

Answers:

As big as a house	As quiet as a mouse
As strong as an ox	As sly as a fox
As quick as a cat	As blind as a bat
As lively as a jig	As fat as a pig
As thin as a rail	As dead as a doornail
As hard as a rock	As proud as a peacock
As harmless as a bark	As happy as a lark
As cross as a bear	As mad as a March hare

As neat as a pin   As ugly as sin
As white as a sheet As red as a beet
As bright as the moon As crazy as a loon
As clear as a bell As deep as a well
As white as snow   As black as a crow

PARENTS IN THE BIBLE

Match each of these persons with the names of his father and mother:

1. Samuel ——— Jacob and Rachael
2. Jacob ——— Abraham and Hagar
3. John the ——— Boaz and Ruth Baptist
4. Seth ——— Joseph and Asenath
5. Joseph ——— Jacob and Leah
6. Obed ——— Abraham and Sarah
7. Isaac ——— Zacharias and Elisabeth
8. Reuben ——— Adam and Eve
9. Ishmael ——— Elkaneh and Hannah
10. Ephraim ——— Isaac and Rebekah

1. Elkaneh and Hannah. 2. Isaac and Rebekah. 3. Zacharias and Elisabeth. 4. Adam and Eve. 5. Jacob and Rachael. 6. Boaz and Ruth. 7. Abraham and Sarah. 8. Jacob and Leah. 9. Abraham and Hagar. 10. Joseph and Asenath.

194

TRICKS

STICK PUZZLES AND TRICKS

While this kind of puzzle is usually called a matchstick puzzle, it can be worked as easily with toothpicks or, on a large surface, with pencils. Matches, if used, should either be burnt ones or the safety type.

1. Remove three sticks from this layout and replace them to form three squares.

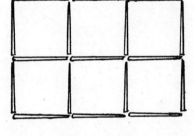

2. Take away six of these seventeen sticks and leave two squares.

3. Take away five sticks and leave three squares.

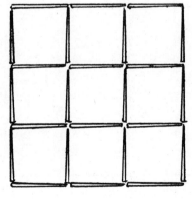

4. Take away eight sticks and leave two squares.

5. Arrange the eight sticks you took away (above) to form two squares and four triangles.

Answers to stick puzzles:

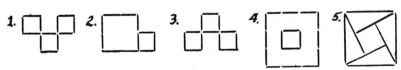

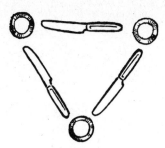

THE BRIDGE

Set three upside-down glasses and three knives on a table as shown. The glasses should be half an inch away from the ends of the knives. Challenge anyone to make a bridge of the three knives that will reach from each glass to the other. The glasses may not be moved.

READING ASHES

Ask each guest to name a famous person. As each name is given, write it on a slip of paper, fold the paper once, and drop it into a metal pan. When all of the slips are in, ask one of the guests to draw a slip from the pan and hold it. Burn the other slips in the pan and then pretend to read the ashes. Announce the name on the slip that has been drawn. The solution lies in writing the same name — the first one given — on every slip. In the meantime you have destroyed the evidence of your deceit.

THE TIGHTROPE WALKER

Stretch a long piece of string across the floor and tell a guest that he is to be a tightrope walker. He must walk the length of the string without stepping off. It looks easy at first, but then make him wear a mask that has slits to see through. And hand him a pair of field glasses which he must hold backwards so that his feet and the string look far away. When he starts to walk on the string, he shouldn't be able to see what goes on around him. Curve the string around so that one end meets the other. See how long it takes before the rope walker realizes that he is going around and around in circles.

A ROPE TRICK

Give a friend a piece of rope about three feet long and ask him to hold an end in each hand. Then challenge him to tie a knot in the rope without letting go of either end. Try as he will, he cannot do it unless he knows the secret of the trick. Fold your arms and tell him over and over how easy it is. When he gives up, have him hand the ends of the rope to you with your arms and

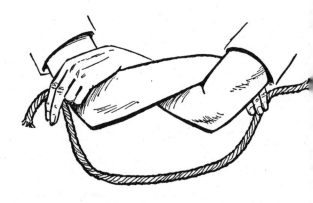

hands held as shown. Unfold your arms and, presto, there is a knot.

A COIN TRICK

Have yourself blindfolded. Then say, "Will one of the ladies please get a quarter from her purse and place it on this table. Be sure to note the date on the coin." When this has been done, ask one of the gentlemen to take a quarter from his pocket, note the date on it, and place it on the table. Just as soon as this has been done, pick up the two coins and note to yourself how much warmer one is than the other. Hold up the colder coin and say. "This is the lady's. The other is the gentle-man's." This trick is almost certain to work because a coin from a man's pocket, where it is close to his body, will be warmer than one from a lady's pocketbook. It is easier to note the difference in temperature with large coins than with small ones.

THE DISAPPEARING COIN

Find two quarters that look almost exactly alike and, if possible, bear the same date. Beforehand, hide one in a bowl or vase in an out-of-the-way place in the room where the audience will be. Press a bit of soft beeswax on a corner of a handkerchief. Then you are ready to perform the trick.

Spread your handkerchief out on a table in front of you with the waxed corner partly hidden under your left hand. Place the second quarter in the center of the handkerchief and then fold in the four corners to meet directly over the coin — with the waxed corner directly on the coin. Press the corners down so the quarter will stick to the wax. Let anyone in your audience feel the coin to make sure it is still there. Now say, "I'm going to make this quarter fly through the air so fast you can't see it. Watch very closely now." Take hold of the two openings of the handkerchief that are nearest you and pull them apart quickly, drawing the quarter up into your hand. Shake out the handkerchief and tell the audience where to look for the quarter. While they do that, slip the other quarter into your pocket.

THE DISAPPEARING KNOT

Tie a simple overhand knot in the middle of a short length of rope, leaving it loose. Then tie the ends of the rope together with several knots, telling your audience that this makes the trick harder. Let anyone examine the rope to make sure all knots are real knots. Tell the audience that you can make the overhand knot in the center of the rope disappear in an instant. With the rope behind your back, quickly run the overhand knot up to disappear into the pile of other knots. Your friends won't know where it went.

CARD TRICKS

The Turn-around

Lay ten cards in a row on a table. Ask someone in the party to turn three of the cards around while you look the other way, and say that you will be able to tell which cards were turned around. You can do this because one end of each card has a wider margin than the other. Be sure to have the ten cards arranged ahead of time with the wider margins all at the top. Then you can quickly tell which were turned.

The Warmest Card

Take about a dozen cards from a deck and fan them out facing the audience. Ask someone to choose a card and point to it. When he does so, pull the card loose from the fan and hand it to him without looking at the face of it. Tell him to hold the card against his forehead for a second to warm it. Then let him place the card with the rest and mix them up. When he hands them back to you, put each one up to your forehead until you pick out the "warmest" one.

Here's how you do it. As you pull out the card chosen by the person who pointed to it, press your thumbnail into the corner of it. This mark is all you need to pick it out as you hold each card in front of you on its way to your forehead.

LASSO THE ICE CUBE

Place an ice cube in a glass of water. Challenge others to get the ice cube out without touching it with their fingers and without using a spoon or any other mechanical device except a piece of string that you hand them. They may try lassoing it, but without success. Hand them a salt shaker and tell them to try putting a little "salt on its tail." When they laugh at this, show them that you can do it. Make sure the end of the string is thoroughly wet

and lay it on top of the ice cube. Sprinkle salt on the cube. Wait a short while and then lift the cube out fastened to the end of the string.

Explanation: Heat flows from the water on the string to the salt water, lowering the temperature of the water on the string until it freezes to the ice cube.

THE GREAT SPUMONI

A Mind-reading Stunt

This act should amuse and amaze guests at a party. The Great Spumoni is introduced by his assistant as the most brilliant mind reader of all time. The assistant is actually the more important member of the act because he has a harder job.

While the Great Spumoni is out of

the room, his assistant puts five different objects in a row on a table. He asks the audience to agree on which the mind reader is to pick out by "reading the thought waves" of the people present. When the object is chosen, the assistant calls in the Great Spumoni. The latter studies the objects thoughtfully. He looks in turn at the forehead of each person in the room as though reading his mind. At last he picks up the object chosen.

This trick works on the basis of signals given in the assistant's words when he calls to the Great Spumoni to come in. If the first object is chosen he says "ready"; for the second, "all ready"; for the third, "we're all ready," etc. — the number of words indicating the object's place in the row.

It's a good idea to let the members of the audience select the objects that are placed on the table.

BOILING WATER IN A PAPER PAN

Tell your audience that you are going to boil water over a flame in an ordinary paper container and they will probably question your sanity. But show them you can do it. Make a box from a sheet of ordinary writing or typing paper that is strong enough to hold water. Fill it with water about a quarter of an inch deep and hold it over a lighted candle, just above the flame. In a short time the water will boil and the paper container will not have burned.

Explanation: The water draws the heat to itself and keeps the paper from getting

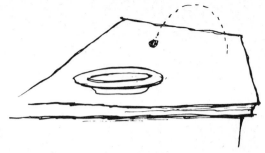

hot enough to burn. Water will boil at 212°F., but most paper must reach a higher temperature before it will catch fire.

THE FLIP-FLOP DIME

Can you blow a dime from a table top into a saucer? It's possible. Place the saucer about six inches from the edge of the table and the dime in front of it, two inches from the edge. Then, holding your chin against the table top, blow hard on the dime until it jumps up. Practice until you know just where to place the saucer and can make the trick work each time you try.

Explanation: The stream of air you blow lowers the air pressure above the dime, and so lifts it. That is why you must blow over the dime and not under it as some watchers may think you are doing.

THE MYSTERIOUS EGG

Tell your audience that you will show them how to get a hard-boiled egg in and out of a milk bottle without splitting it. Let anyone who thinks it's easy try to push the egg into the bottle. You may have to get another egg to use, but you will have proved your point that the trick isn't as easy as it looks.

Now crumple up a piece of paper, set it on fire and drop it into the bottle.

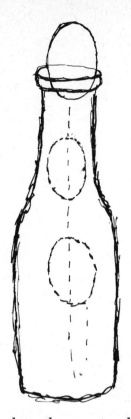

TONGUE TWISTERS

Two tutors who tooted the flute,
Tried to tutor two tutors to toot.
Said the two to the tutors,
"Is it harder to toot,
Or to tutor two tutors to toot?"

Three gray geese in the green grass grazing; gray were the geese and green was the grazing.

She sells sea shells down by the seashore.

Tie twine to three tree twigs.

Peter Piper picked a peck of pickled peppers; a peck of pickled peppers Peter Piper picked. If Peter Piper picked a peck of pickled peppers, where are the pickled peppers Peter Piper picked?

How much wood would a woodchuck chuck if a woodchuck would chuck wood?

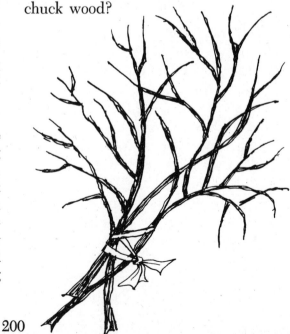

Quickly place the egg on the neck of the bottle with its pointed end downward. In short order the egg will plop into the bottle. Next, try to shake the egg out of the bottle to show that this can't be done. Rinse out the ashes of the burnt paper. Then hold up the bottle so that the egg slides down into the neck. Keeping the bottle tilted up, blow into it as hard as you can. Out will come the egg.

Explanation: Pressure of air inside the bottle makes it impossible to force the egg in. But by heating the air in the bottle, you made the air expand and some of it escaped. As the remaining air cooled when the flame went out, greater pressure outside the bottle forced the egg in. Then by blowing hard into the bottle you increased the inside pressure and pushed the egg out.

Fanny Finch fried five floundering fish for Frances Fowler's father.

The sixth sheik's sixth sheep's sick.

The brain teasers, tricks, and tongue twisters (except for "Two Tutors") have been selected from *The Giant Book of Family Fun and Games*, by Jack Tedford, published by Franklin Watts, Inc.

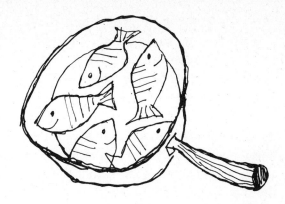

THE NEW SECOND AVENUE TROLLEY LINE

Eleanor Estes

The four Moffat children — Joey, Sylvie, Jane, and Rufus — lived with their Mama in a yellow house on New Dollar Street in Cranbury. Their Papa had died when Rufus was just a tiny baby. Times were hard, and it was often difficult to make both ends meet, but there was always plenty of love and laughter in the yellow house. And such good times — as when three of the Moffats took a ride on the new trolley.

HURRAH! school was all over until next September. Sylvie had left this morning for a week's vacation at Camp Lincoln. The other three children were on their way over to Sandy Beach, a small beach on the harbor at the other end of town altogether. They were going to spend the day there and had sandwiches and fruit for a picnic lunch. Mama was the only one left at home in the yellow house and she was sneezing her head off with hay fever and trying to finish a dress for Miss Chichester so the children might have another year at the dancing school.

The children loved to go to Sandy Beach. They loved to look out across the harbor that lay like a great pool of water at the feet of the Sleeping Giant and of East Rock and West Rock. They

hoped to find a lot of the little pink and white shells. If they did they would make a necklace for Mama, Jane thought.

It used to be such a long walk over to Sandy Beach. So long that Rufus used to have to be dragged half the way in his express wagon, he'd get so tired. But now it was nothing to get there. The new Second Avenue trolley line whisked you there in just no time at all. If you were lucky, that is, and the motorman did not have to wait at the switch for the trolley that was coming from the other direction to get past him.

There was a switch at this end and a switch at the Sandy Beach end of the line. Sometimes the motorman was able to get all the way to the switch at the Sandy Beach end before the other trolley came along. That was when you were lucky. But more often than not the red light was on at this end of the line, the red light that said, "Hold! Wait there. Here comes the other car."

Then you had to wait so long you might just as well have walked in the first place. Still, the whole town agreed it was a fine thing, very modern, to have this new trolley line. Because the Sandy Beach end of town was so hard to reach otherwise. And you could bring a book or your knitting to pass the time when you had to wait at the switch.

"Here," Mama said as she kissed them good-by. "Here is a nickel for each one of you. Don't be gallivantin' all over town. Go straight to Sandy Beach and have a good time!" she called, waving her blue checked apron after them.

"Good-by," screamed Jane to Mama. "Don't let those Murdocks buy our house. Lock the doors and pretend you

aren't home if they come back again."

"Come on, Jane," said Rufus, always impatient to be off. "What are you goin' to do with your five cents?"

Five cents apiece! They were of two minds as to what to do with it. They might spend it on an ice-cream cone or they might take the new Second Avenue trolley to Sandy Beach. Joe was all in favor of an ice-cream cone. Jane too. But Rufus had never been on the new Second Avenue trolley line. He preferred spending his five cents that way.

"I may be a motorman when I grow up," he said. "And I'd like to see how they run."

"You've been on trolleys before," said Joe. "They all run alike."

"No," said Rufus. "There's this business about the red lights. I want to see how they handle that. There's two tracks everywhere else, 'n' there's just one track here. S'different."

"But I want a cone," said Joe.

"Well," said Rufus with finality. "I'm goin' to spend my five cents on the new Second Avenue line. I don't mind goin' alone."

"Oh, well. Let's all go that way then," said Jane. "It *is* fun to ride on the trolley and we'll have more time at the beach."

"All right," agreed Joe, although he still felt somewhat reluctant. However, later on, he was glad he had agreed to this because of the strange doings that followed.

The three sat down on the curb at Second Avenue to wait for the trolley. They picked the tinfoil out of several empty cigarette cases and chewing gum wrappers they found in the gutter. Joe rolled it up in a hard ball and put it in his pocket. Jane found a piece of colored red glass and they all took turns looking at one another and at the sky through this. When the trolley came, they got on and gave the motorman their five-cent pieces. The motorman handed Rufus' five cents back to him.

"You don't have to pay, young man. Not till you're six," he said.

Well, six was just exactly what Rufus was now, but he saw no good in arguing the point at this moment. He put the five cents back in his pocket and gave Joe and Jane a rather triumphant glance.

There were very few people on the trolley. They were all sitting near the back and they were all very calm. Apparently they were quite accustomed

to the new Second Avenue line and thought no more of riding on it than of the milkman delivering a bottle of milk every morning at their door. But Joe, Jane, and Rufus all sat in the front seat as near the motorman as possible. They looked at the signal at the side of the road. The light was green. Good! They would not have to wait for the trolley coming in the opposite direction. The motorman started the car. But look! Just as he stepped on the motor power, the red light flashed on! It meant Stop! But did he stop? He did not! A baleful look came over his face and he steered the car right off the switch and onto the main track. What was the matter with the man? The light said "Stop" and he went!

A murmur of surprise ran through the trolley. But the motorman heeded this not at all. Up Second Avenue he steered the trolley, stepping on the bell like anything every time he saw a dog, and muttering to himself the whole way. The children watched him in fascination.

"Makes me wait every time, does he?" he was saying to himself. "Makes me wait every day down here. *He's* supposed to wait up there at the other switch once't in a while. 'I'll tell the chief,' I said to him. 'Tell the chief,' he said to me. Tell the chief I did. 'Fight it out for yourself,' he said to me. I'll show 'im! I'll show 'im!"

The children looked at one another. Excitement! They looked ahead. Way, way down the car line, under the arch of elm trees, they could see it now! Could see the other trolley coming right towards them! Just a little speck

203

it was at the other end of Second Avenue. But bigger and bigger as it drew near. The nearer it came, the more excitedly the motorman clumped down on his bell. Pretty soon they were near enough to hear the other motorman clump down on *his* bell.

Although their hearts began to beat fast, Joe, Jane, and Rufus said and did nothing. The others in the trolley, roused out of their lethargy, first ran to the motorman and implored him to stop. But the motorman was deaf to all entreaties. So the passengers all ran to the back of the car to get as far as possible from what looked like an inevitable crash. Some uttered silent prayers.

And imagine what this looked like to people along Second Avenue! Windows were thrown up and amazed heads stuck out of them. Everybody on the street stopped to stare and wave their arms about in excitement. Old Mrs. Squire, who was carrying a basket of apples to her nephew, grew so frantic she actually threw apples at the

motorman and screamed, "Go back, go back."

Such a thing was unheard of! Two trolleys on the same track, one going north, the other going south, could do only one thing — meet with a crash. And how ridiculous in broad daylight! If there were a fog now, like in London, that would be a different matter; but broad daylight! That's what all the people thought, anyway.

"Go back! Go back!" The cry was taken up by everyone along the street, some running to one car, some to the other, trying by emphatic waves of the

arms to indicate what they meant, as though the motormen were altogether deaf or else quite daft. There was some talk of calling out the Fire Department. Finally Mrs. Squire did sound the alarm. "A hose will do much," she screamed.

All these people did not reckon, though, on the motorman. For he had a head on his shoulders. And so, for that matter, did the enemy motorman. But how good his head was and whether he'd choose to use it, that was the question.

The nearer the two cars came to one another the slower they ran, although both motormen kept up that hulla-baloo of clumping down on the bells. Finally they were just edging toward one another like great tawny tigers at bay. At last they came to a dead stop, nose to nose, just as the hook and ladder arrived.

Now what would happen? Joe, Jane, and Rufus were shivery with tense excitement. Yes, it had required a great deal of nerve and trust in their motor-

man not to jump off when things looked so bad a while back.

"They oughta have pistols or a sword to fight it out," said Rufus.

But they didn't need pistols. Their tongues did quite well. Such a row there was as quiet Second Avenue had never before heard. Mrs. Squire said she would write a letter of complaint to the newspaper and recommend that the new Second Avenue line be removed. The town of Cranbury had

gotten along for centuries without it and could again. Newfangled notions, these one-man trolleys with their one-track contraptions! But no one paid any attention to her. They were listening to the motormen. Except for the firemen, of course. They were crawling over and under the two trolleys looking for the fire. And everyone was listening too hard to what the motormen were saying to tell them that there was no fire.

The Moffats' motorman was an old man with a walrus mustache. He wore his hat straight over his eyes and took this business of driving a trolley car very seriously. The enemy trolley had a young motorman who wore his hat tipped on the back of his head and sat all slouchy on his stool. Yes, the picture of impudence.

"Hey, you old sardine, you!" he bawled in a most insulting tone of voice. "You were supposed to wait. What's a matter with your eyes? Didn't ya see the red light?"

"Yeh, you young whippersnapper. I saw the light all right, all right. Same's I do every trip. And I'm sick of seein' those red lights, see? You're supposed to wait up there at the upper switch half the time. At least until two-thirty. Do you ever do it? No, you do not. My people wants to git home, just as much as your'n wants to be off. It's a fifty-fifty proposition. Now back up your car to the other switch or I'll . . ."

And he edged his car an inch nearer, menacingly.

"Why, you old sardine . . ." sputtered the other.

More angry words followed but the

205

young motorman could see the old one would never yield an inch. On the contrary, he was getting in such a dither he was all but climbing out of the front end of his trolley to shake his fist in the other man's face. Goodness knows what a man of his temperament might not do. Moreover, the worst of it was the old geezer was right. Chief had just said to him the other day, "Look here, O'Brien. On the two-thirty trolley you're supposed to wait for old Mc-Cann at the upper switch until two-thirty on the dot. If he's not there then, you can go. Otherwise wait, get me?"

Oh, it was clear the young motorman did not have a leg to stand on. Moreover, the sentiment of all the onlookers was on the old motorman's side. So he said, "All right, you old sardine, you. But you'll hear from the Chief about this. Endangerin' the lives of the citizens of Cranbury, that's what it amounts to."

Then he tipped his hat still farther back on his forehead. He assumed an air of great nonchalance and took the driving gear to the other end of his trolley. The firemen cleared the way, and Motorman O'Brien, defeated, started back the way he had come, old McCann following close behind, all but butting him in the rear like an angry bull. The people cheered. The firemen sounded their siren and went back to the firehouse. Mrs. Squire looked around for some of her apples to take to her nephew, but the little boys had gotten most of them. The yellow dogs ran up the street after the yellow trolleys, yelping and growling.

At last the enemy O'Brien's trolley

was safely lodged on the side switch and the Moffats' trolley sailed triumphantly up the track to Sandy Beach where Joe, Jane, and Rufus got off. Phew! That had been a ride and worth a nickel, if not more!

Nothing that happened that afternoon — swimming, ducking, digging for clams, catching snails — nothing could come up to that trolley ride. That trolley ride! There was something to tell Mama about!

Conclusion:

In the book *The Moffats,* by Eleanor Estes, published by Harcourt, Brace and Company, you can go on to read about the *two* signs that came to be nailed on the yellow house. One said "For Sale" and the other said "Scarlet Fever."

THE HORN THAT STOPPED THE BAND

Arthur H. Parsons, Jr.

When a horn won't play properly something must be done at once. Terry did it.

IT WAS A most peculiar noise. It wasn't exactly a rumble and it most certainly wasn't a squeak. It was more like the sound of three mud pies dropping on a hot sidewalk on a summer afternoon —
PHLOO . . . PHLOO . . . PHLOOF.
And it came right out of the big round shiny end of Terry's French horn.

The drummer heard it first and laid down his drumsticks. Then the trumpet player heard it and took his trumpet from his lips. The saxophonist and the triangle player heard it together and stopped their playing. Soon even Miss Burbank, who directed the Monroe School Band, heard it and stopped waving her green baton with the light on its end.

At last Terry himself heard it —
PHLOO . . . PHLOO . . . PHLOOF . . .
and he put down his French horn. But it was different with Terry than with the others, for when he heard it his face went all red — not just the red that comes from blowing hard and long, but the red that comes when your French horn goes —
PHLOO . . . PHLOO . . . PHLOOF.

Miss Burbank knew that it would do no good to scold Terry, because there was really nothing that he had done. She drew a deep breath and blew on the horn. It went —
PHLOO . . . PHLOO . . . PHLOOF.

Then the saxophonist tried it and it went —
PHLOO . . . PHLOO . . . PHLOOF.
It even went —
PHLOO . . . PHLOO . . . PHLOO . . . PHLOO . . . PHLOOF for the tuba player, who was big and fat and rolypoly and who could blow longer and harder and louder than anybody else in the whole school band.

There was nothing to do, Miss Burbank told them a little bit sadly, but for Terry to take the French horn to Mr. McWhinnery, who was the school principal and who could fix ANYTHING. Maybe he could find the trouble.

So down to the office went Terry, lugging his French horn under his arm

207

and looking not nearly so red as he had when his music first stopped the band.

"Please," he said in a small voice to Mr. McWhinnery, "can you stop my French horn from going PHLOOF, so our band can have its rehearsal?"

But that red look came again when Mr. McWhinnery put the mouthpiece to his lips, swelled himself up like a big fat frog and B-L-E-w! For there it was once more —
PHLOO . . . PHLOO . . . PHLOOF . . .
but this time louder than ever, and more rumbly than ever.

Mr. McWhinnery took the horn first on his right side, then on his left side, and then right in his middle, and blew again —
PHLOO . . . PHLOO . . . PHLOOF.
Then he pulled the horn apart, first one slide, then another, and then another, and he looked in each one and he shook each one. Then he put them together again, first one slide, then another, and then another. Then he blew

again, but twice as hard and twice as long as the first time —
PHLOO . . . PHLOO . . . PHLOO . . .
   PHLOO . . . PHLOOF.

"There's nothing to do," Mr. Mc-Whinnery told Terry, who was now as red as the inside of a cherry pie, "but to take it to Mr. Swaggart who plays the French horn in the All-City Brass Band. Certainly he'll be able to find out what's wrong with it."

So Terry put his horn in the case, hooked the strap that held it tightly, locked the case, and started downtown to see Mr. Swaggart. At first he didn't like the idea very much. He didn't know Mr. Swaggart and what's more, Mr. Swaggart didn't know him.

"Probably," Terry thought, "he'll just laugh at me and send me home."

But then Terry remembered what a wonderful band the All-City Brass Band was and how happy the men always looked when they were dressed up in their red and white uniforms in the Fourth of July parades. He remembered that Mr. Swaggart must have

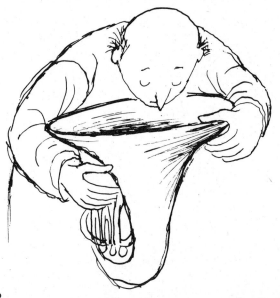

been a boy once, and maybe he once had a French horn that went PHLOOF. If he did, well then — well — anyway that was the most important bit of remembering that Terry had done all day, and it made him feel much better.

In fact, he felt so much better that he took out his French horn right there on the bus and blew it loudly just to make sure it was still going —

PHLOO . . . PHLOO . . . PHLOOF.

He tried it only once, though, because he saw everyone on the bus looking at him in a very strange way, and the bus driver the strangest of all.

By the time he came to the hall where the All-City Brass Band rehearsed, Terry was feeling very proud of his horn and its peculiar noise. He went right up to Mr. Swaggart who, with the other musicians, had just returned from a big band concert, and he said,

"My French horn is acting very silly. It just goes PHLOOF no matter what I do. Can you tell me what's the matter with it?"

Mr. Swaggart, who was a jolly man, laughed a loud laugh and answered in a most friendly voice,

"Now don't worry, my little man,

just one blow by old man Swaggart on this little old French horn and we'll have it fixed in a jiffy."

He put the horn to his lips; he breathed in and he breathed out. And as Mr. Swaggart breathed out and as he pressed on the keys, Terry realized that he was playing with no trouble at all Terry's own French horn part in "Parade of the Wooden Soldiers."

As Mr. Swaggart played on, the other men in the band watched with smiles on their faces. Terry didn't know whether to be glad his horn was fixed or sad, because he had just begun to think that all this was fun, when suddenly he heard as before that familiar —

PHLOO . . . PHLOO . . . PHLOOF.

Mr. Swaggart wasn't at all pleased and he wasn't at all jolly any more, especially when he saw the rest of the band laughing, because — who could tell? — maybe they were laughing at him. And because he didn't like being laughed at he decided not to try to fix the horn, for maybe — who could tell?

there — not even a man who can play a double bassoon — who cares about a silly French horn that can only go — PHLOO . . . PHLOO . . . PHLOOF."

But he knew that Miss Burbank was depending on him, and so were Mr. McWhinnery and the drummer and the tuba player and all the rest of his school band. And maybe even Mr. Swaggart. Who could tell?

Slowly, very slowly, Terry started up the long flight of steps. Slowly, very slowly, he pulled open the big wooden doors and walked into the hall.

There, a long way off, down past row after row after row of empty seats he saw a stage and on the stage he saw a great big man in shirt sleeves waving a baton. Sure enough, there was the Symphony Orchestra rehearsing for its big concert.

There were men with violins, men with trombones and saxophones, and men with trumpets. A drummer was beating on his drum and a man was playing the piano. There was a French-horn player and there was even a pretty lady with a harp.

All those people and all that beautiful music they were playing made Terry feel smaller than ever. But he remembered Miss Burbank and his own band again and slowly, very slowly, he moved down the aisle until he came to what looked like a comfortable seat way down front. There he sat down and wiped his face with the back of his hand.

He sat there through four pieces. He listened to Mr. Vanivoff scold his orchestra. He watched Mr. Vanivoff bring beautiful music out of all those

— maybe they would laugh at him even more. Besides, all at once he remembered a most important telephone call he had to make, and he rushed off, shouting at Terry,

"You'd better take your horn down to Mr. Vanivoff, the leader of the Symphony Orchestra. He can play any instrument there is, even a double bassoon. Certainly he'll be able to find out what's wrong with your French horn."

So, a little sadly, Terry again put his French horn in the case, hooked the strap that held it tightly, locked the case, and started down the street to find Mr. Vanivoff. When he reached the enormous Symphony Hall with all the carving on the front and the big wooden doors, he had a queer feeling way down in his stomach.

"Surely," he thought, "that's much too important a building for a boy my size to enter. Surely there's nobody in

different instruments. And he began to wish that he played the piano instead of the French horn, for nobody, he thought, would ever have to carry a piano all over the city.

And as he giggled, then smothered the giggle, then giggled again at the very idea of lugging a piano around, Mr. Vanivoff turned, stared at him with his mouth open, then stopped the orchestra.

"Enough, men, enough," he said in a deep, cross-sounding voice that sent shivers right up and down through Terry's body. "Let us see what our young visitor wants. Perhaps he wants a lesson, no?"

"No," Terry answered in a small jiggly voice, "I don't want a lesson. I only want someone to stop my French horn from going PHLOOF every time I play it."

Mr. Vanivoff looked just a tiny bit angry as he shouted,

"You come to me, Vladimir Petrovitch Vanivoff, with a little thing like that? Give me the horn. I will fix it, then you go home and do not bother me again, no?"

Terry climbed up the narrow steps at one side of the stage. When he reached the very center of the stage, he passed the horn to Mr. Vanivoff, who took it quickly and gave one blow. And then right out of its big round shiny end came one great big —

P-H-L-O-O-F.

The men in the orchestra knew better than to laugh. They even knew better than to stay around, and in almost no time at all they had left the stage. Mr. Vanivoff himself looked as

red as Terry had the first time he heard the noise. But Mr. Vanivoff would not give up as Mr. Swaggart had done.

"No French horn," he shouted in that terrible deep voice of his, "can put anything over on Vladimir Petrovitch Vanivoff."

And he blew again loud and long.

But long and loud the French horn answered —

PHLOO . . . PHLOO . . . PHLOOF!

Mr. Vanivoff put the horn down on the floor, grabbed Terry's hand, and led him off the stage.

"Come, my friend," he said, "I have a book that will tell us what to do — a book that will tell us how to stop all this foolishness of PHLOOF's."

With that he marched off, his heels making a loud clicking sound in that big empty hall.

"Now," thought Terry as he found himself being almost dragged off the stage, "we'll surely find out what's wrong and just what it is that makes a French horn go —
PHLOO . . . PHLOO . . . PHLOOF."

Just as he was thinking this he heard a sound, a most beautiful sound — the sound, mellow and soft, that a French horn makes when there's nothing wrong with it. This sound wasn't really music, but it wasn't any PHLOOF either. Jerking away from Mr. Vanivoff, Terry rushed back to the stage.

There he found a funny little man with a mustache, dressed in faded blue overalls, blowing on the French horn and pressing on the keys as though he were having the most fun he had ever had in his life.

```
                LOO
      TOO          POO
POO          TOO   POO
                LOO
```

went the French horn and the little man's eyes twinkled with every POO and every TOO and even with every LOO.

As Terry rushed up, his French horn gave one last loud POO-O-O and the little man, who was the Symphony Hall's janitor, grinned at him. Then he held out his hand and said,

"Would you believe it, young feller, when I blew on this here horn, what do you suppose happened? Right out of the end of it came this here pea. I don't know what you'll do with it, but it's yours if you want it."

But Terry didn't want the pea, not even for his pea-shooter. He reached for his horn, put it to his lips, and started blowing. He played "The Stars and Stripes Forever" all the way through without a single PHLOOF. Then he started to play "Parade of the Wooden Soldiers" and as he did he heard something else. He heard the high tones of some violins and the deep BOOM of a drum. He heard the soft music of a piano and the stirring call of some trumpets. He even heard a tinkly-sounding harp and the POO-TOO-LOO-POO of another French horn.

As he looked around, there was Vladimir Petrovitch Vanivoff wearing a big smile and leading with his baton the whole Symphony Orchestra who by now were playing "Parade of the Wooden Soldiers" right along with Terry himself.

Terry tried to smile as he played, to show how happy he was, and the lady harp player smiled right back at him. He looked out of the corner of his eyes at the drummer, and the drummer winked a great big wink as he beat away at his drum. Then Terry looked straight at the Symphony Orchestra's own French-horn player, who took his horn from his lips and smiled the biggest, broadest smile of all. HE really WAS proud!

But he wasn't half so proud as Terry himself was, to be playing his own French horn right along with the famous Symphony Orchestra and its leader, Vladimir Petrovitch Vanivoff.

Conclusion:

Many exciting pictures for this story can be seen in the book *The Horn That Stopped the Band*, by Arthur H. Parsons, Jr., published by Franklin Watts, Inc.

212

PART III

THE CLIMB

Carolyn Treffinger

Although his father is a fisherman by trade, Li Lun is terribly afraid of the sea. When the day comes for all the ten-year-olds to go out on their man-making trip, Li Lun refuses. His father, promising the boy a land task that will make him beg for the sea, gives Li Lun seven grains of rice to be planted at the top of Sorrow Mountain. "And don't come back," warns the father, "until you have grown seven times as many grains as I have given you."

IT WAS THE HOUR of short shadows. Li Lun trudged steadily upward over an unbroken trail across what was once melted rock or lava. Like other village children he had often climbed half the height of Lao Shan to gather salt from the rock holes. Li Lun was grateful that the children who were gathering salt today were at home now, having their noonday meal. He would not have to hear their taunts. In an hour he would be out of their sight. He must hurry if he were going to reach the mountaintop before dark.

Sharp-edged stones cut his feet. Setting down his load he slipped into his straw sandals.

Up he climbed, past the place of the rock holes used by the villagers to catch rain water for their tea. Along the shelflike lava rocks he climbed ever higher and higher.

Perspiration trickled across his forehead and into his eyes. He set down the bundles to wipe away the moisture and to rest.

Ships and sampans were coming and going on the sea. But not his father's sampan. It was far away by this time.

If only his father had understood why he could not go to sea! Li Lun felt sad in his heart that he had disappointed his father. But he shuddered at the thought of deep waters climbing into the sampans.

He stood up and shouldered the bundles again, happy that he was toiling up the mountain instead of sailing over the sea. The rocks were at peace among themselves; the waves were not.

Li Lun struggled upward until the bundles on his small back seemed like another mountain pushing him down. He balanced the pole on a rock and

Might the rats be evil spirits following him up the mountain? Li Lun wondered. He poked a bamboo pole at one of the places where he saw a rat. "I will have to let them know that I do not want them," he told himself. "The bamboo poles are good for this!"

Up and up Li Lun clambered and rested, clambered and rested. While he relaxed, his eyes followed the gulls skimming over the water and back to shore. Swiftlets flying in and out of the rock holes along the mountain walls attracted his attention. They were building nests and caring for their families. He knew these were the little birds that built the lovely pink-and-white nests which the city shopkeepers collected for bird-nest soup. Li Lun smiled. He would hunt some of the nests and dry them. If he did not eat them, he could sell them later to the shops. There would be plenty of time.

He shouldered his burdens and continued the ascent. The sun shone hot upon the lava over which he trod. There was no well-defined path. Here and there grasses and hardy weeds had dared to grow in the cracks which scarred the rocky surface. A few bushes and even trees had gained a foothold.

By now his sandals were worn so

crawled from under it to rest. With his gourd cup he dipped water from a rock hole to quench his thirst.

While he rested, Li Lun looked in the huge pocket of his jacket to see that the rice kernels were still there. He must not lose them. And the dragon bones. He was relieved to find them both safe.

When he took up his load again, Li Lun wondered about the bamboo poles. They were so clumsy to carry that he was tempted to leave them behind. But his mother had said that he might need them, so he picked them up.

Lizards scurried across the trail to get out of his way. Gray rats poked their heads from behind brown rocks. They were so like the stones that Li Lun would not have seen them except for their curious beady eyes.

smooth that Li Lun slipped frequently. Then he came to a spot where he must either climb up over a rocky ledge or crawl more than his length along the height of a cliff. This he must do by hanging fast to scrubby bush growths.

Li Lun set down his bundles for breathing time. At the west the sun shone upon the water just a mountaintop above it. He must not rest too long.

As he gazed at the sea, Li Lun wondered again about the fishermen. Where were they? He looked at the ledge and at the cliff. At least there was not an evil spirit sitting atop a wave and waiting to crash down upon his head! The thought so encouraged him that he got up, eager to go on. He stretched his arms upward. The ledge, he found, was too high for him to lift his bundles onto it. He must span the cliff. It overlooked the water and sloped upward at a dizzy angle.

Li Lun decided to try the climb first without his bundles. He took hold of some scrubby growths and pulled. They held firmly. He went on, testing each bush before he trusted his weight to it. At last he stood, trembling, on firm rock.

Li Lun burst into a shout of exultation. He was across! The sea was below, but it had not got him! Looking ahead, he saw that he was almost at the top of Lao Shan.

Now he must bring his bundles. Cautiously he recrossed the sloping cliff.

The carrying pole with bundles attached might trip him, he decided. So he carefully loosed the bundles from it. He wondered if he could throw the bamboo poles across. He made a trial of one of them. It landed safely and did not rebound. He threw the other one. Then the carrying pole. Not a grain of soil escaped from the mat! He threw the bedding roll. Then the clothing.

Now to cross again himself. With the precious bundle of food in his right hand, Li Lun clung to the bushes with his left. Putting his right foot ahead to safe footing, he braced the bundle against it until he could move his left foot forward. Every move he made he guarded. On the last step his right foot slipped a little, but the bushes held firmly.

Li Lun lifted the food to the ledge and pulled himself up beside it. Gratefully he sat down among his belongings. He looked out over the dark green sea. The sea that he had conquered from high places.

" 'There are other things than fishing!' " Sun Ling's words sounded in his ears above the swell of waves against the rocks far below.

Hurriedly Li Lun retied his bundles to the poles. Then, with a lighter heart, he shouldered the poles and set off again, whistling.

A short way ahead the mountaintop looked as if it had been scooped out. There stood a rocky wall to the right as high as an ocean wave. To the left the wall was only as tall as a sampan. Between the two walls was the rocky mountain floor, about as wide as a fishing boat is long.

At last he had reached the top!

But what a reception! Gulls screeched and screamed all about him.

Dropping his bundles, Li Lun walked cautiously toward the sky wall so that he would know what was beyond. Sharp and rugged rocks bit at his feet. He did not go near the edge of the cliff, which sloped abruptly down into the sea. That was the door which the gulls used, coming and going.

Deep blue and purple shadows had already settled over the face of the water, but the light rays still brightened the mountaintop.

Where would he sleep? Not a blade of grass or a bush was in sight. Only screaming gulls and rock holes. Rock holes with water in them!

Li Lun walked around, looking for a ledge under which he could crawl for shelter. He could not sleep out in the open. The gulls would think that he was a rock and roost on him!

The wind blew chill through the sea-gull door. Li Lun pulled his padded jacket about him more tightly as he walked along the low wall. There was not a spot where he could sleep. He crossed over to the higher wall and continued his search.

Dark gradually closed in about him, like a gray mist creeping up from the blackening waters.

Then he noticed that the gulls were investigating his bundles. Had they smelled the rice? he wondered. Or the shrimp? They might peck holes in the cloth. Hurriedly he stumbled across the rocky floor and drove them away.

When he looked up again, Li Lun saw a dark shadow along the opposite high wall. It was only waist-high, but he struggled over the uneven surface to examine its possibilities.

Sure enough, it was an opening into the rock! Gulls flew out as Li Lun climbed up.

"You will have to find another place to sleep!" challenged Li Lun. "I need this spot, and it is too dark to hunt another."

The cave was about as deep as he was tall, and it had a smaller opening on the face of the rock.

Li Lun pushed the gulls' eggs to the wall of the small cave and dragged over his bundles. He opened his bedroll and, hugging the bundle of rice with both arms, sank exhausted upon his strange bed.

Conclusion:

The perilous climb was only one of many dangers that Li Lun encountered in carrying out his difficult task. Read about the others in *Li Lun, Lad of Courage*, by Carolyn Treffinger, published by Abingdon Press.

SIMBA'S FIRST LION

Alden G. Stevens

Simba is a boy of the Wanyamlima, or People of the Mountain, who live in Tanganyika in East Africa. When he was very tiny his father killed a lion and rubbed the fat of the beast on the boy's head to make him brave. The name Simba means "lion." Simba lives in the midst of constant danger from wild beasts and has need of all the courage and daring he can muster.

PERHAPS NO PLACE in all the world is as beautiful as East Central Africa on a dewy morning just after the season of long rains. Mountaintops, forest, and veldt are gilded with the gentle light of the newly risen sun. Millions of flowers make masses of color on the face of the plains. Across the vast sweep of the land, zebra, wildebeeste, kongoni, and gazelle — numbering beyond the power to count — feed into the wind. High against the blue heavens, vultures wheel on motionless wings.

On such a morning, at the hour of letting out of cattle, which the People of the Mountain call *mafungulia*, the boy, Simba, stood near the gate of his mud-walled village. In his hand was a herding spear about five feet long. About him were other boys of his own age equipped with similar spears, and all of them were shouting at the cattle which were crowding through the narrow opening in the wall. Occasionally, when some wayward cow would turn back into the village itself, a boy would leap nimbly after her, prodding her sides and yelling shrilly until she would turn, with tossing horns and rolling

eyes, to join the others on their way through the gate.

Dust rose in clouds. Simba's slender body was covered with it, for it clung to the sweat that rolled down his ribs and stomach. For a week now, Simba had been entrusted with the responsibility of herding his father's animals and he was a proud boy. He was no longer a child. With his hunting bow he could bring down a monkey from the tallest tree, driving the bamboo arrow clean through its body. Across hard ground he could track game by way of signs only visible to eyes trained to observe the tiniest details — a scratch

217

on the rocks, a turned pebble, a blade of grass out of place. Watching the skilled warriors of his village, listening to the tales of his people, trained by his father, he had learned the things that would get him food and save his life from savage men and beasts. Simba was only eleven years old and his body was the slender, slim-muscled one of a boy, but he knew and could do many things, for his school had been the hard one of his race, savage and primitive, where death and hunger and suffering are the price of mistakes.

Finally, with low bellowings, the cattle were all out in the open and the boys started cutting out their own particular cows from the herd. Wielding his spear industriously, Simba darted into and about the milling beasts, avoiding horns and trampling hoofs, pricking the stubborn ones, joining his shrill voice with the cries of his companions until magically, it seemed, some sort of order began to appear and the cattle were sorted into family groups. Driven by their sweaty brown herders, they began moving off toward the hills, where they would graze all day on the grassy hillsides. When the shadows of the mountains began to creep across the plains, they would be driven back again to spend the night where no lions or leopards could kill them, safe in their *zizi* within the thorn and mud walls of the village.

Most of the boys joined their herds and moved away in groups of three or four, but Simba started out alone. Some of the boys called to him to ask that he go with them, but he shook his head. He liked to play the games of the vil-

lage with his friends and did not ordinarily like to be alone, but this guarding of his father's property was a new and great responsibility. With the other boys, he might not watch closely, and a hyena could kill and carry off one of the young calves. So he preferred to be alone, and run no risk of being distracted from his herding.

Simba strode along behind his herd of some twenty humpbacked cows with three or four calves straggling at their mothers' heels. His objective was a long slope of sun-drenched hill a mile distant. From the top of it he would be able to look to the northward over the plains and forest strips while his cattle grazed in plain view before him.

Arrived finally at the hilltop, Simba sat down in the grass, his spear beside him. The animals fed close to him in little groups down the slope. Sitting there, Simba looked out over the land he knew so well. Partridges and spur fowl rustled through the grass about him. The plains were dotted with feeding game. At his left a few yards, tiny gazelles frisked on the hillside. Far below, at the edge of the jungle that bordered a stream, five giraffe moved majestically along the forest back-

ground where great clumps of poinsettia flamed against the green foliage. Simba's eyes took in all this in a sweeping glance, coming to rest again on the feeding cattle. With special fondness he watched Madoadoa and her calf. The little creature was only five days old. Madoadoa, the spotted one, was his mother. She was a large raffish-looking cow with no apparent sense of her maternal responsibilities. When the calf tried to get at her udders to feed she would swing coyly away from him, never ceasing her own greedy cropping of the grass, while the little fellow stumbled constantly after her, bawling forlornly for the dinner that was rightfully his.

Simba became quite annoyed at Madoadoa, at thus keeping her calf hungry and unfed. Simba loved this calf with passionate devotion. It was his very own, presented to him by his father the day it was born, but there was nothing he could do at the moment to change Madoadoa's casual treatment of her offspring, so he lay back on his elbow and gave himself to the thoughts and daydreams of his age.

Perhaps it was because his stomach was full of *posho,* or it may have been the warmth of the equatorial sun and the coolness of the grass roots, but at any rate, the truth must be told that Simba's head nodded and he fell asleep. He had not slept long when he woke suddenly, guiltily conscious that he had failed in his duty. Suddenly he was aware, with the instinct of all wild creatures, that he was not alone. He rose in a single lithe movement and whirled, the slender spear in his hand. There,

immediately behind him stood old Kibeti, the dwarfed cripple. His cavernous black eyes fixed the boy sternly. Ashamed, Simba relaxed and sat down. Kibeti limped forward and sat beside him.

"So," grunted the old man, "you sleep while guarding your father's cattle. Had I been a lion I could have killed you, and killed that worthless Madoadoa as well."

"I am sorry, Kibeti," replied Simba. "I deserve to be eaten by a lion. Perhaps you will tell my father and he will beat me." He eyed Kibeti anxiously.

"This time I will not tell him. You are young, and it is hard for the young to sit still through the long day. To sit without sleeping, here in the sun, is hard for a boy. Perhaps I should say that it is hard for a child, because a boy who would be a hunter and a warrior would not sleep."

Simba's cheeks burned with shame, for he knew that there was justice in what Kibeti said. "Oh, Kibeti," he said miserably, "I know well that what you say is true. If the warrior who sits by the village night fire should sleep, then enemies could enter our village and spear us on our mats where we slumber. I will never sleep again when I should stay awake."

219

"That is well and as it should be," said Kibeti. "Listen now, and I will tell you of my younger days when I was a great warrior. Do not look surprised, Simba, for indeed I was truly a hunter and a fighter in our tribe. Of course the time was before the elephant caught me and made me a twisted man. He broke me with his trunk and left me as you see me now." The old man's face cracked into a bitter smile as he looked down at his withered legs, which lay like black, broken sticks on the grass before him.

Simba smiled gravely. "We have many warriors and hunters, Kibeti. If the elephant had not broken you with his trunk, then you would not be a teller of stories. There would be no man then, to tell us magic things. Who but Kibeti can sit with the chiefs in council to tell them of the things that happened long ago so they may know how to deal with these same matters when they happen now?"

Kibeti nodded complacently. "Perhaps you are right, my boy. As you say, I am indeed a great man, but sometimes I think it is better to be young and strong than it is to be great." The old man's eyes burned in the wrinkled mask of his face as he thought of the days of his youth.

Presently he spoke again. "I had almost forgotten that I wanted to speak to you of duty," he continued. "There is the duty of the hunter who follows a long hard trail so that his people may have meat. There is the duty of women, they who cook and raise our crops, of the warrior who watches and sleeps not, lest enemies come in the night.

And then too, there is the duty of the boy who watches his father's cattle. He must not sleep. Now me, I never sleep except at night. Old though I am, I never — I never —" Kibeti's voice trailed away and stopped. His head nodded and the aged body relaxed. He slept.

It was very still there on the sunny hilltop. Simba smiled and looked at Kibeti as he slept, noting the gray color of his wrinkled skin where ashes from his fire clung to it. He looked at the twisted, broken body and thought of the elephant who had made Kibeti a cripple. Simba made a note in his mind to ask for the story some day soon. It was one that Kibeti had never told. Thus musing, the moments passed until Simba bethought him of the cattle. He looked up and surveyed them.

Apparently all was as it should be. Scattered down the gentle slope of hill, the beasts grazed contentedly. All of them except Madoadoa and her calf were within safe range. She, however, had wandered further down the hill apart from the rest. Beside her, the calf was still fumbling for his dinner. Simba watched the two, debating with himself the advisability of going after her and driving her back with her companions. As he watched, suddenly his

eyes became slits and his head shot forward. Showing above the grass some thirty feet from Madoadoa and her calf, were two black spots. They were about a foot apart. Now Simba knew that two such motionless black spots as these were not a natural part of the landscape. As the fact of their being there swiftly became part of his consciousness, he instantly knew what they were and his heart contracted with fear. He was looking at the black tips of a lion's ears. The lion was carefully stalking Madoadoa, and the calf that Simba loved. It would only be a matter of a short time now — when Madoadoa had fed a bit closer to the crouching lion — that a blaring snarl would shatter the peace on the sunny hillside and a tawny shape of death would hurtle from the grass upon Madoadoa and the calf. She and the little one would go down in a welter of blood.

Only the whisper of wind through the grass and the soft breathing of Kibeti broke the silence. The boy Simba sat there in the clutch of paralyzing fear. If he moved and the lion saw him, would the great beast attack him? If he stepped between the lion and his prey, then would the lion charge him in a swift, awful rush? Would he go down under the lion's spring, down with a scream as great claws ripped the flesh from his bones and long fangs met in a crushing bite at his spinal column? All these questions flashed through Simba's mind and fear kept him crouching there, shaken and trembling.

Just then the calf bawled softly. Simba peered at him and his mother. They were now a little closer to those two black spots at the grasstops. Any instant now it would happen, here before his eyes. Then as he looked, seeing the calf at last successful, nursing at his gaunt mother's udders, a great love for them brought a mist to his eyes. And at that instant when he ceased thinking of himself and his own fears, and thought of his love for those two so close to death, some measure of fright left him. He poked Kibeti, grasped his little spear, and rose to his feet.

The old man got up and stood beside him. At once he took in the situation. "Down, Simba," he whispered. "Down, or we too will die."

"No, Kibeti, I am going forward," cried Simba. "Have I not my spear?" He raised the slender, inadequate weapon above his head.

As his voice broke the silence, Simba stepped forward. Unarmed and afraid, the ancient warrior went with him. Side by side these two, the shuffling crippled one and the slim brown boy, advanced toward Madoadoa. Simba shouted bravely, although his voice quavered a bit. His legs trembled and there was a strange shaking in the pit of his stomach.

The instant Simba's voice rang out, the lion stood up from the grass. He knew he was discovered and he growled deeply in his throat. Madoadoa now saw the danger that menaced her and her calf. If in the past few days, she had appeared to be a poor sort of mother, she made up for her sins in this moment. Swiftly she thrust the calf behind her. Her eyes rolled with terror, but she stood firm between her calf and the lion, horns down, ready to give her life for the little creature cowering in terror behind her.

Simba advanced steadily. The lion, at sight of these human enemies, bared his fangs and crouched to face them. Less than forty feet now separated the man and boy from the great muscular beast before them. It was close enough. Simba halted, placed the shaft of the spear under his right arm, advanced the sharp tip, and braced himself. Lower the lion crouched and dropped his shaggy head. It was the sign of a charge. In that moment, Simba knew for certain that the spear would break under the impact of the lion's spring, knew that he was going to die, he and old Kibeti, there on the green veldt grass. The lion rasped out a snarl and Simba saw the mighty muscles gather themselves in coiling masses for the spring.

And at this moment Madoadoa let go a furious bellow, put down her head, and charged at the lion. It was so unexpected that Simba dropped his spear. The lion may have remembered suddenly that the scar on his shoulder had come from the dagger-like point of a mother eland's horn. Perhaps a quick recollection of the pain of that old deep wound flashed across his mind. At any rate, his savage form lifted in a mighty leap and he hung for a moment in arched splendor against the sky. When he came down to earth, he turned in a flash and went off down the hill in long bounds to disappear in the forest below. Madoadoa stood, shaking her horns, and bawled defiance after the fleeing lion. The calf, now over his fright and quite unaware that his mother had narrowly escaped committing suicide, was sucking happily at her udder. Kibeti and Simba sat down and laughed until tears came to their eyes. Through the afternoon Simba watched the cattle, and when the long shadows drew across the plains from the mountains, drove them back to his village.

That night the tale was told by Kibeti and all the people heard it. Warriors looked at Simba appraisingly, for they knew he would some day be a great one among them. The boys with whom he played looked too, and with a respect they did not quite understand. If Simba's chest swelled a bit and if there was a slight strut to his walk that night, he must surely be forgiven. After all, the thing he had done had taken the courage of a man and a warrior.

Conclusion:

In the book *Lion Boy, a Story of East Africa*, by Alden G. Stevens, published by J. B. Lippincott Company, Simba escapes death many times. In one exciting chapter he saves the life of a white boy at the risk of his own.

THE VILLAGE OVER THE MOUNTAIN

by Julia L. Sauer

Greta had always loved the fog, although she had never quite understood why. But one foggy day on the Old Post Road a surrey came by with a woman whose plum-colored dress rustled "like a three-master coming up in the wind," and Greta knew that in Blue Cove, where no house had stood for a hundred years, she would find what she was seeking.

TWO GIANT BOULDERS stood where the old Post Road left the plateau and began to wind down toward the sea. The road had insisted on squeezing between them when it might just as easily have gone around. Greta had often traced the scorings on their inner surfaces, the straight lines that marked the years of travel. The rocks loomed ahead in the fog. It was exciting to think of dashing between them behind these brisk horses. She gripped the side of the surrey and leaned forward. The woman beside her gave a short laugh and reached for the whip.

"Never fear, child. We'll make it," she said. "They're the sentinels that guard Blue Cove. None passes but has a right there." She paused. "But *they* pass safely," she added.

"Have *I* a right there, do you think?" Somehow the question had to be asked. The woman turned to look down squarely into the girl's face.

"You've no cause to worry. You've the look of one that was always welcome there," she said curtly. Then the horses took all her attention. The boulders were upon them, dark shadows in the mist. The horses lunged through, then settled quietly again to a steadier pace.

Greta knew what this part of the mountain was like in clear weather. To the south of the road there was still un-

broken forest — scarred here and there with burned patches, but otherwise dark, mysterious, treacherous, with unexpected chasms. Along the edge of the road to the north a high protective hedge of spruce and alder had been left, cut here and there with entrances. Beyond the hedge lay a clearing that sloped gently toward the sea. And dotting this clearing were cellar holes. Smooth little depressions they were; covered with the quick-springing growth of the pasture. It looked almost as if the homes of the departed inhabitants had sunk quietly into the earth.

Greta had often played in these cellar holes. It was fun to imagine where each house had stood, where the doorways had been, where the single street had led. Sometimes the shape of the depressions gave a clue; often a flat stone marked a doorstep. Once she had dug up a tiny spoon in a cellar hole. A salt spoon it was, with a strange name engraved on the handle. Her father said it was the name of a packet that had gone down off the Islands, years and years ago. The little salt spoon was one of her most treasured possessions, kept carefully hidden under the handkerchiefs in her dresser drawer.

Suddenly the woman pulled the team to a stop. They were opposite one of the entrances to the clearing. "You'd best get out here," she said abruptly.

Greta climbed quickly over the wheel. In front of her an archway, hung with its curtain of fog, opened into the clearing. But did it lead into the familiar pasture? Or did it lead to something very different? For the first time in all her wandering in the fog she hesitated. She turned back toward the surrey for reassurance. The woman was smiling at her now, kindly, all her grimness gone.

"Go on," she said gently. "In the second house you'll find Retha Morrill. You two will pull well together."

She touched the horses with her whip. Greta watched the surrey disappear into the thicker mists below. Then, with a pounding heart, she stepped through the arch of spruces.

Her feet crunched on gravel. She was walking on a neat path. At her right loomed a big barn. Beyond she traced the outlines of a house — small, neat, gray-shingled — and another, and another. A smell of wood smoke was in the air. Something brushed against her ankle. She looked down. A gray cat, the largest she had ever seen was looking at her pleasantly.

"You beauty," Greta said to her and

224

stooped to stroke the long hair. But it was one thing to greet a guest and quite another to be touched. Without loss of dignity, without haste, the gray cat was simply beyond reach. But she was leading the way, her plume of a tail erect. Where the second neat path turned off toward a house the cat looked back to be sure that Greta was following. Suddenly a door banged. Around the side of the house and down the path a little girl came running. She stopped when she saw Greta and gathered the cat into her arms. The two girls stood looking at each other.

"I'm Retha Morrill," said the Blue Cove child slowly, "and I think that Princess must have brought you." She smiled and took Greta's hand. "I'm glad you've come. Let's — let's go in to Mother."

Greta could think of nothing to say. She could only smile back and follow. But she knew, and Retha knew, that as the woman had said, they would pull well together. At the doorway Retha dropped Princess on the wide stone before the steps.

"Please wait here," she said. "I'll find Mother."

Greta nodded. She still wasn't sure of her voice. She watched Princess curl into a graceful heap on the stone — gray stone, gray fur, gray mist, gray shingles, all softly blending and blurring before her eyes. She knew that stone well. It had strange markings on it. She had often traced them with her finger where it lay in the empty pasture beside her favorite cellar hole.

There was a brisk step inside the house and a tall woman stood in the

doorway. "Come in, child, come in," she began. Then she stopped and looked long at her visitor. And Greta looked up at her. She had never seen such blue eyes in all her life before — nor such *seeing* eyes. They were eyes that would always see through and beyond — even through the close mist of the fog itself. The woman put out her hand and drew Greta inside before she spoke again. Her voice was a little unsteady but very gentle.

"You are from over the mountain," she said. "I can tell. And I'd know it even if this were the sunniest day in the year."

Greta didn't quite know what the words meant but she knew somehow in her heart that she and this strange woman would understand each other without words. In just the flash of a moment they had traveled the longest road in the world — the road that leads from eye to eye.

"I am Laura Morrill," Retha's mother continued quietly. "Retha shouldn't have left you standing outside — not such a welcome guest. Now turn toward the light and let me look at you. Humph! Yes. You *must* be an Addington. Would your name be Greta, now? Yes?" She laughed. "So I guessed it right the very first time! Well, you have the Addington look and the Addington eyes, and there's always a Greta among the Addingtons! Yes, and there's always a child among the Addingtons that loves the fog it was born to. You're that child, I take it, in your generation." Her laughing face grew sober and she gave Greta a long, steady look. Then she smiled again quickly and smoothed back Greta's hair with a quick stroke of her hand.

"It's the things you were born to that give you satisfaction in this world, Greta. Leastwise, that's what I think. And maybe the fog's one of them. Not happiness, mind! Satisfaction isn't always happiness by a long sight; then again, it isn't sorrow either. But the rocks and the spruces and the fogs of your own land are things that nourish you. You can always have them, no matter what else you find or what else you lose. Now run along and let Retha show you the village. You two must get acquainted."

"May I leave my pail here?" Greta asked her. "I picked quite a few berries for Mother, coming over."

"Of course you may," Laura Morrill told her. "But that reminds me! You must be hungry. We're through our dinner long since but I'll get you something. I dare say you left home early."

"I brought a sandwich to eat on the way," Greta told her. "Only there hasn't been time."

"Sit right down and eat it here, then. Retha, you fetch a glass of milk and I'll get you a piece of strawberry pie. Retha went berrying early this morning, too, and I made my first wild strawberry pie of the season."

After Greta had eaten she and Retha went out to explore the village. Its single street followed the curve of the shore line. There were houses on only one side, with patches of gardens behind white fences. Across the road in a narrow stretch of meadow, cows were grazing. Thick spruces hedged the meadow in at the lower side where there was a sharp drop, almost a precipice, to the shore. But the street was high enough so that Greta knew on a clear day you could look from the houses straight out to the open sea.

It was pleasant walking slowly up the street with Retha, but Greta couldn't find anything to say. To ask questions might break the spell. She might find herself back again in the empty clearing. And Retha knew that it would be impolite to question a stranger. They reached the end of the street before either spoke.

"That's our school, and there's our church," Retha said. She pointed out the little white building across the end of the street next to the neat church with its steeple.

"The shore curves in here, and there's another bay down there where you can find all sorts of things to play with. Our church is nice. Sometime maybe you'll be here on a Sunday so you can see it inside. There isn't any burying ground," she added. "It's all rock here and we can't have our own. When folks die they have to go over the mountain to be buried. Now let's

go back to the Post Road and I'll show you the shore and the wharf and the fish houses and the stores."

In one of the door yards two very small children were playing. As they came near Greta saw that there was a man seated on the ground, his back against the fence. One child tripped and sat down heavily, jolting out an indignant wail. The man reached out a long arm. He set the small thing on its feet again as you would set a ninepin, and gave it a comforting pat. The wail died suddenly and the man slumped back. Greta laughed.

"He must like children," she said, "or they must like him. Why, he didn't even have to speak to that one."

"Sss-h," Retha warned her. "He *can't* speak, but we — we don't know — for sure — whether he can hear."

Whether he heard or only felt their approaching footsteps, the man turned suddenly and looked up at them between the pickets. A lean, dark, strange, and foreign face. The eyes were piercing, searching. Greta found she was standing quite still, giving this strange man a chance to look at her. Retha didn't seem to think it unusual. She was smiling at him and saying slowly,

"Anthony, this is my friend Greta Addington. She's from over the mountain." Then she pulled Greta gently away. The man turned to watch until they faded into the fog.

"But, Retha, you said he couldn't *hear*, and then you *spoke* to him. And he looks almost — almost savage. And still he was minding those babies."

"I said we don't *know* whether he

hears or not. Or whether he could speak if he wanted to. But he's not savage. He only looks that way when he sees a stranger. I guess it's because he's always trying to find someone — someone he knows, I mean. But, Greta, did you see his — his legs?"

"I didn't see anything but his eyes. And anyhow, he was almost hidden in that clump of monkshood. What about his legs?"

"He — he hasn't any," Retha said quietly.

"Hasn't any *legs?*" Greta could only stare in horror.

"They are gone just above his knees, so all he can do is crawl, and mind babies. But no matter how fierce he looks, *they* understand him. And he's always gentle."

"But what happened?"

Retha hesitated a moment. "We don't talk about him much. I'd like to ask Mother first if I should tell you. Let's go down to the wharf now." And Greta had to be content.

When they reached the Post Road, Retha pointed toward the shore. "See! The fog's lifting a little. You can see the end of the wharf from here and you couldn't see anything an hour ago. Come on."

Greta stood still. She couldn't explain it even to herself, but suddenly she knew how Cinderella felt when the first strike of midnight began to sound.

"I think there isn't time to go down today, Retha," she said. "But I'd like to go next time I come. I must go home now. It'll be late when I get over the mountain."

"Your berries! You left your pail at

our house," Retha reminded her.

They ran back to the house. In the doorway Mrs. Morrill stood holding the pail.

"The fog's lifting," she said quietly and held out the pail. "I put a piece of strawberry pie on top of your berries, but I don't think it'll crush them any. And come again, child. We'd like to see you often; that is, if your mother doesn't worry. You're like a visitor from another world." Then she added as an afterthought, "Coming as you do from over the mountain."

Greta thanked her and took the pail. Retha went as far as the Post Road with her. They said good-by hurriedly.

Greta left without daring to turn back and wave.

It was almost clear when she reached home, but late. Her mother greeted her with relief. Father had finished milking and sat reading the paper. Greta's conscience hurt her. She hadn't once thought of the mail and someone else had gone to the post office. She held out the pail to her mother.

"There's a surprise in it, Mother," she said. Gertrude opened the pail.

"I *am* surprised," she said. "I never dreamed you'd find so many. It's early yet for strawberries."

Greta stood very still. Then she stepped over and looked into the pail. There were the berries she had picked. *But there was nothing else in the pail!*

Suddenly she wanted to cry, but her father was looking at her over the top of his paper. He was smiling at her just with his eyes, but he looked as if he understood.

"Fog thick at Blue Cove today?" he asked.

"Heavens, child, have you been way over there?" asked her mother.

How did Father know she had been to Blue Cove? Greta no longer wanted to cry. She could look back at Father and almost smile.

"Yes, Father," she said. "It was very thick today."

"I thought so," he answered and went back to his paper.

Conclusion:

In *Fog Magic* by Julia L. Sauer, published by The Viking Press, Greta finds that foggy days are truly magical, and returns again and again to the village and the life of its inhabitants.

THE FAST SOONER HOUND

Arna Bontemps and Jack Conroy

American folklore is rich in "tall tales" about lumberjacks, cowboys, roustabouts, and other colorful characters whose fantastic exploits make us swell with pride and double up with laughter. This story spoofs the early railroading days of our country, and the hero is a hound dog whose feats deserve to be set down for posterity.

A RAILROAD MAN was walking down the street with his hands in his overall pockets, and a long-legged, lop-eared hound trotted behind him. The man was smoking a pipe. After a while he stopped walking, took the pipe out

of his mouth, and turned to the hound.

"Well, Sooner," he said, "here's the place."

They had come to a small building near the railroad tracks. Over the front door was a sign which said *Roadmaster*. The dog called Sooner didn't seem to pay much attention to the man's words; but when the man opened the door, the hound followed him inside.

The man in the office looked up from his desk. "What do you want?" he asked.

"I'm a Boomer fireman," the railroad man said, "and I'm looking for a job."

"So you're a Boomer! Well, I know what that means. You go from one railroad to another."

"That's right," the man in overalls answered proudly. "Last year I shoveled coal on the Katy. Before that I worked for the Frisco line. Before that it was the Wabash. I travel light, I travel far, and I don't let any grass grow under my feet."

"We might be able to use you on one of our trains," said the Roadmaster. "Have you got some place you can leave the dog?"

"Leave my dog!" cried the Boomer, knocking the ashes out of his pipe. "Listen here, Mr. Roadmaster, that Sooner always goes along with me."

"He does, eh? And why do you call him a Sooner?"

"He'd sooner run than eat — that's why. I raised him from a pup, and he ain't ever spent a night or a day or even an hour away from me. He'd cry fit to break his heart if we weren't together. He'd cry so loud you couldn't hear yourself think."

"I don't see how I can give you a job with the hound," the Roadmaster said. "It's against the rules of the railroad to allow a passenger in the cab. Makes no difference if it's man or beast, nobody is allowed to ride with the fireman and the engineer in the cab, and no passenger is allowed in the caboose. That's Rule Number One on this road, and it's never been broken yet. What's more, it never will be broken as long as I'm Roadmaster. So it looks as if that Sooner is going to spoil things for you."

"Why, he ain't no trouble," said the Boomer. "He don't have to ride in the cab. He just runs alongside the train. When I'm on a freight train, he chases

230

around a little in the fields to pass the time away. Sometimes he scares up a rabbit — just to play with when things get dull. But he ain't no trouble to nobody, and he never rides in the cab or the caboose."

"You mean that old hungry-looking hound can out-run a freight train?" The Roadmaster laughed. "You can't make me believe that!"

"Shucks — he'll do it without half trying," said the Boomer proudly. "Matter of fact, it will be a little bit tiresome on him having to travel so slow, but that Sooner will put up with anything just to stay close by me. He loves me that much."

"Oh, come now," said the Roadmaster. "The dog isn't born that can outrun one of our freight trains. We run the fastest freights from coast to coast. That's why we get so much business. I'm sorry we can't give you a job. You look like a man that could keep a boiler popping off on an uphill grade, but I just don't see how we can work it with the hound."

"Listen," said the Boomer. "I'll lay my first pay check against a dollar bill that Sooner will run circles around your freight train. What's more, he'll be as fresh as a daisy when we pull into the junction, and his tongue won't even be hanging out. Of course, he'll want to trot around the station about a hundred times before we start — just to limber up, you know."

"It's a bet," said the Roadmaster, "and you can have the job. I'm not a mean man, you know, but Rule One has got to stick."

So the Boomer fireman climbed into a cab beside the engineer and began to shovel coal for all he was worth. The freight train pulled out of the station and started to pick up speed. The Sooner loped along beside it. In no time at all he had left the freight train far behind. Sometimes he would pop out of sight in the underbrush along the tracks in search of rabbits or squirrels. But before long he could be seen up ahead, waiting for the train to catch up. Once the Boomer looked out of the cab and saw a strange look on the hound's face. The Engineer noticed it too.

"What's the matter with your Sooner?" the Engineer asked. "He looks worried."

"That's right," the Boomer said. "He's worried about the hog law. That's the law that says we can't work more than sixteen hours on this run. If that happens we'll have to stop this train in the middle of the fields and wait for a fresh crew to take our places. I reckon that Sooner thinks we're going to get in trouble running so slow."

"Why, this ain't slow!" exclaimed the Engineer. "This engine is doing all it can. The boiler is hot enough to pop."

"Well, it ain't no speed for my Sooner," the Boomer laughed.

The freight train made its run and then returned, but the Sooner led it all the way. And when the dog trotted into the Roadmaster's office a mile ahead of the train, the Roadmaster got angry. He knew right away that he had lost his bet, but he didn't mind that. What he minded was what people would say about a freight train that couldn't keep up with a long-legged, lop-eared Sooner hound. They would say the train wasn't any good. The Roadmaster couldn't put up with such talk as that. No, sir. His freight trains must keep the name of being the fastest in the country.

"Look here, Boomer," he said, as the fireman climbed down from the cab. "You won the bet. That Sooner out-ran the freight train, but I'm going to transfer you to a local passenger run. What do you think about that?"

"Suits me," said the Boomer. "Me and my Sooner ain't choicy. We take the jobs we get, and we always stay together."

"You think the hound can keep up with our passenger train?"

"He'll do it easy," said the Boomer. "No trouble at all."

"If he beats our local, there'll be two

dollars waiting for you when you get back. That Sooner is faster than he looks, but I don't believe he can beat a passenger train."

Conclusion:

In the book *The Fast Sooner Hound*, by Arna Bontemps and Jack Conroy, published by Houghton Mifflin Company, Sooner races many other trains, including the famous Cannon Ball.

A SUNDAY HORSE

Glen Rounds

When Uncle Torwal and ten-year-old Whitey first noticed the blind colt out on the range, the older man wanted to shoot it. He was sure the handicapped critter would fall in a hole or get "wolf et." But Whitey, certain the colt was too smart for that, begged for its life and hoped some day to tame it for a Sunday horse. As the months went by, the boy and his dog Confusion watched the colt's progress with satisfaction. Then came the heavy snows, and one day the blind colt stumbled into the shelter maintained for the ranch horses. Most of the tame horses tried to run him out, but he made friends with old Spot.

ALWAYS, NOW, the blind colt was waiting for Whitey at the corral gate, anxious to smell his pockets to see what he'd brought him.

The colt was pretty well pleased with the new way of living. Whitey and Spot were both friends and he had all he wanted to eat. He'd even gotten used to Confusion who at first reminded him of a coyote because of the

size of his noises and the smell of his fur. He knew now that the dog was harmless, and they even played games, chasing one another around the corral.

One day Whitey brought a piece of rope with him and when the colt came up he let him smell it thoroughly, and rubbed his back and sides with it.

Before long he was able to dangle an end of it over the colt's back without his trying to buck it off. The next thing was to make a rope hackamore and slip it over the colt's head and fasten it. After he was used to that it was a simple matter to teach him to lead. Of course, all this took time, but Whitey didn't begrudge a bit of it, and whenever he thought about the excitement he'd cause when he went out

around the country riding his new horse and making him do tricks to amaze folks, he broke out in goose-pimples all over.

Whitey's spending so much time playing with the colt and talking to him made Confusion kind of jealous so he always got as close under their feet as he could while they were busy. And one day Whitey got him an idea as he watched the colt and the dog touching noses. He carefully picked the dog up and set him on the colt's back.

The dog and the colt were both startled at first, but Whitey rubbed the colt's head and talked to him until he quieted down enough to turn his head

and smell the dog. As for Confusion, he was quite pleased with himself and sat up on the colt's broad back and grinned his long-tongued grin like a circus dog. The colt finally got so he'd let him jump up and ride around the corral on his back anytime.

After he'd taught the colt to lead, and had him gentle enough that he would let himself be curried all over and have his feet picked up, Whitey decided it was time to teach him to come when he whistled. He turned the

233

colt and Spot out of the corral and let them graze in the pasture awhile. Then he would rattle the oats in the pan and whistle. Hearing the oats both horses would come trotting.

Before long they learned to come when he whistled whether he rattled oats or not. For an hour or so every afternoon he turned them out to graze, while he watched that they didn't get out where Uncle Torwal might happen to see them.

One afternoon he was sitting on top of the old corral fence watching Spot and the colt busy grazing some distance off and thinking how lucky he was that Uncle Torwal hadn't found out what he was doing.

He was just in the middle of deciding that he'd show the colt at the county fair in the fall as a "High School Horse," and was listening to the crowds in the grandstand hollering with excitement at seeing the blind colt jump through a flaming hoop with him on his back when he was interrupted.

"What's that little crow-bait doin' in the pasture here, Bub?"

Uncle Torwal had ridden up from the other side, and Whitey had been so busy with his county fair imaginings that he hadn't heard him.

"Oh, he's jest grazin' with ol' Spot," Whitey said after he had pulled himself together. "Ain't he a purty scamp, though?"

Uncle Torwal got off his horse and climbed up on the fence beside Whitey before he answered. Then he took his jack knife out of his pocket and settled down to whittling like he was going to spend the afternoon horse trading.

"He is a right likely lookin' piece of horseflesh, for a fact," he said after a while. "Too durn bad he's blind, ain't it?"

"You bet he's purty!" Whitey said, and he wondered what he should say next. He knew that the time had come for a showdown, but he also knew that Uncle Torwal had his horse trading humor on and that there was no use coming straight out and asking him anything. So he decided to horse trade too, and he took his jack knife out and pried a whittling stick off one of the corral poles while he waited for Uncle Torwal to make the next move.

"Him an' Spot act like they was ol' friends. Kinda looks like the colt musta been in here quite a spell," Torwal said after a while.

"Yessir, it does kinda look that way for a fact," Whitey agreed, and whittled busily.

"Wouldn't be surprised if maybe he drifted in during the blizzard," Uncle Torwal went on.

Whitey knew that all this had nothing to do with whether he could keep the colt or not. Uncle Torwal was just playing cat and mouse with him, and he'd have a lot better chance of keeping the colt if he could keep on acting like a horse trader. So he tipped his old hat a little farther down over his eyes and whittled some more, like he wasn't worried at all.

"Yessir, that's probably just about what happened," Whitey said.

"Now that he's made up to ol' Spot the way he has it's kinda too bad we gotta shag him back out on the range again," Uncle Torwal said.

"Yeah, it does seem kinda too bad, don't it?"

"Of course, if he was gentle an' knowed anything, it'd be different," Torwal went on. "But you take a crittur raised wild like he was, and bein' blind too, I doubt that a feller would ever be able to do anything with him."

"But you figger that if he could be gentled he might make a good Sunday Horse?" Whitey asked, grinning privately to himself.

"Well, I dunno," Torwal said. "But when I was a kid I had a blind saddle mare, and she was a dandy. Sure-footed as a goat, she was. An' never ran into nuthin'."

"But she was extry smart," he added after a little thought.

"This colt is mighty smart, just like I always said!" Whitey exclaimed.

"Well, he did manage not t' get wolf et, or fall into nuthin'," Torwal agreed. "But that was prob'ly jest luck. It don't mean he could learn anything else."

Whitey saw that now was the time for him to get busy if he wanted to keep the colt. So he slid down off the fence.

"Watch this," he said, and whistled shrilly.

The colt stopped his grazing and came trotting up. When he got close he smelled Torwal and snorted and stopped. Whitey called him and the colt came on, keeping his ears pointed at Torwal, however, and snorting a little.

Whitey fed the colt a handful of oats and put the hackamore on him and rubbed his hands all over him and picked up his feet, one by one, to show that he was gentle, like he'd seen horse traders do.

Uncle Torwal sat quietly so as not to upset the colt.

Then Whitey called Confusion and patted the colt's back. Confusion came running and jumped to his place on the colt's back.

"How you like this, Uncle Torwal?" Whitey asked as he led the colt up with Confusion still riding.

"Well, I'll be dogged!" Torwal exclaimed. "Don't know as I ever seen anything like it, before."

"Oh, he's a smart feller, all right," Whitey said, grinning fit to split his face.

"Durned if he ain't," Torwal agreed. "Kin he do anything else?"

Whitey had hoped Uncle Torwal would ask that, because he had spent a lot of time teaching the colt a special trick for just such an occasion.

He turned to the colt. "Do you think you could ever learn to be a fancy saddle horse?" he asked him, and scratched him lightly between the fore-legs. The colt nodded his head up and down.

"You ain't going to be any trouble to anybody, are you?" he asked him again, and at the same time he scratched the colt's shoulder. The colt shook his head sidewise.

"See that, Uncle Torwal! He can even talk!"

"Durned if he can't!" Torwal grinned. "Reckon he's smarter than I figgered."

"Yessir!" said Whitey. "An' he'll learn to do a lot of other things, too!"

Uncle Torwal climbed down off the fence and walked over to his horse.

"Well, you better bring him home and put him in the calf pasture if you

figger on keepin' him," he said as he climbed into the saddle.

"Yessir! I'll bring him right over!" Whitey said.

Conclusion:

The book *The Blind Colt*, by Glen Rounds, published by Holiday House, also tells about the time the blind colt and his mother had to fight it out with a pack of wolves and the time the colt became trapped in the mud at the water hole.

MEPH, THE PET SKUNK

John L. George and Jean George

During a spring storm the mother skunk had carried her babies from their rain-flooded den to a dry haven under the summer kitchen. One kit died, but the other one lived to be discovered by Sycamore Will, who heard the scratching clear up in the kitchen. Sycamore isn't allowed to have a dog because dogs eat too much, but he hopes his father will let him raise the skunk as a pet.

MEPH crouched in the dark corner for many minutes before he forgot his scare. His mother was out hunting and Meph was hungry, in fact more hungry than scared. He paced out of the shadows and circled the inside of the foundation, stopping again and again to dig in the dirt. His long front claws sank deep, but they found no food. Then he climbed over the tumbled rocks in the foundation and looked out through the hole to the afternoon world. Yellow dandelions were bobbing on their pale hollow stems, and the green pokeweeds were now as tall as the foundation. Meph crouched there a long time, watching the life beyond the dusty summer

kitchen. Nearby a song sparrow was sitting motionless on her second clutch of eggs. Meph could see the grassy nest woven into the lilac bush. From down in the swamp her mate called. He was telling her that the swamp was quiet, and that no predators were near and to come join him in gathering food. His whistle was bubbling and sweet in the warm June air. When he was done, Meph saw the female turn her head. The sun flashed in her eye. Mouselike she slipped from the nest, and flitted down the hill.

Meph looked down at his feet and bit the dirt that was lodged between his toes. The dropping sun was framed in the little doorway. He watched the bees dart past him on their routes to and from the alfalfa field. Presently the song sparrow returned to her nest, glanced swiftly around, and slipped down on her eggs. A few minutes later a slender grass snake came writhing through the tall grasses. It lifted a third of its body high, and struck. A strumming grasshopper was snapped through the snake's mouth. Meph saw a bulge as it moved down the elastic throat. He sniffed the sharp odor of the snake, blinked, and closed his eyes. When he opened them again he found that he was sniffing a pleasant

wind that came up from the marsh. He rose excitedly and looked down the hill, for the wind bore the rich scent of his mother. She was walking home, her head low, her haunches high, and her tail lifted. Unlike the mother song sparrow she needed no all-clear signals before she went hunting, for she was endowed by nature with a great protection, and feared little or nothing.

Meph tumbled through the hole in the stone wall and ran to meet her. He sank his nose into the black fur and smelled deeply of her wonderful odor. She herded him back to their den. She could smell Sycamore Will riding the tractor up and down the corn rows, and although she did not fear him for herself, she wanted her kit sheltered.

Inside the gloomy walls, she played with the energetic kit, letting him pounce on her and roll her over, biting at him gently now and then to tease him, and chuttering with approval as he stamped his feet for her and lifted high his tail.

Up to this point Meph had been an easy kit to raise. He had obeyed her warnings, stayed in the nest when she left, and had made little noise. Now, however, she sensed a change in him. He was ready for new things. His curiosity was growing and he was becoming discontented with the small space under the summer kitchen. He fussed and chortled more in the evenings. He played harder and often looked out the entrance toward the mountains and the stream.

The mother also understood that much of Meph's restlessness was due to her. Her milk was not enough for

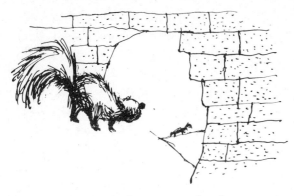

him. Making a living on the farm was difficult. The sterile washed soil did not harbor many nourishing insects or mice. The young barn owls were catching the mice near the house that had been her main source of food. She found herself hunting longer and longer, farther and farther away, yet getting less and less to eat. This affected her supply of milk for Meph. He was too young to take hunting, too vulnerable to the hungry fox of the field, and the insatiable owlets. Yet she understood his needs and knew that she must take him out tonight.

It was a hectic evening for the mother skunk, but a glorious one for Meph. Without benefit of words, he knew his mother was permitting him to follow her this night. He bounced happily behind her to the hole in the wall. He lifted his regal tail and clambered out into the moonlit yard. He sensed his mother's uneasiness as she moved cautiously into the shadow of the house. Meph knew he was to hunt. He looked around, listened, then spurted out into the moonlight after a May beetle. It had blundered into a blade of grass. It paused a moment then climbed slowly up the blade, its yellow wings sticking out from under

the chestnut brown covers. Meph was about to nose it when his mother pounced on him and herded him back into the shadow of the farmhouse. Meph followed at her heels.

At the far corner of the summer kitchen they left the dark shadow of the Lites' home and slipped through the tall grass, downhill to the swamp. Frequently Meph's mother turned on him, bit him, and growled. He immediately turned away from the dark trails that led off through the swamp and decided not to explore. The mother knew her kit was not schooled in discipline, and what he must know to protect himself must be learned in a hurry. At times she seemed to bite and snarl at him for no reason at all, but by the time they reached the Yellow Breeches Creek, Meph was not starting off alone on the trails he found.

The Yellow Breeches rolled quietly within its banks, no longer the swelling stream that had driven them from their home. Many years ago it had flowed constantly all year. Bass had lived in its clear pools. However, as the farmers cut and grazed their woodlots, the trees could no longer hold back the soil, and silt filled the pools. As the fields were exposed by poor farming, the rains carried the topsoil into the stream, and the bright water turned muddy. As the bass died off, so passed the sleek and beautiful minks. The otter disappeared and the deer moved to the brushlands of the mountains. All the wild animals were affected by the farmers who tilled the soil without thought or care.

The lonely night heron stalked the

shallows spearing the sluggish suckers, the fish of unhealthy waters.

Meph trotted out to the stream bank, and the night heron lifted its great wings and flew up the creek. He watched it disappear, then waddled down to the water with his mother. She pulled snails from the muddy stream, crunched them, and gave them to Meph.

The sensation of solid food surprised Meph. It did not slip down his throat like milk, but stuck against his tongue and teeth. He churned it around and around in his mouth, then suddenly the food lodged far back on his tongue, slipped, and was gone. He took another snail from his mother and chewed at it as she did. Sweet juices pleased him; he romped forward for more.

Meph ate snails and beetle larvae until he was comfortable, then turned to other things. With the wet point of his nose pressed close to the ground, he wandered up the stream bed. He blundered into an old log that smelled of ants and centipedes. His mother called to him. Meph was young, and obedience was hard to learn. He pushed under the twisted log and squeezed out on the other side. He stopped and peered under the log to see if his mother was following. Above him sounded the click of claws. Meph looked up to see his mother on top of the log. He squeaked and ran. He ran as fast as his short legs would carry him, bright-eyed and excited by the knowledge that any instant his mother would catch him. When she was almost upon him, he turned to the left and bumped head first into the bank. Knowing he was cornered, he lifted his

tail and turned his head to see where his haunches were. With his tail in firing position he felt confident and secure. He contracted the muscles that controlled his scent anal glands. He waited for the wonderful odor to come from his body. Nothing happened. The night air still smelled of the muddy stream bottom and rotting leaves. There was a hammering thud and Meph was looking into the angry eyes of his mother. She was pounding the ground with her front feet. With a deft swat she struck Meph and he tumbled over against the bank. Scolding, gabbling, and snapping she drove him back to the stream. Meph sat quietly on the bank. From time to time his mother snapped at him as if to refresh his memory.

Conclusion:

In the book *Meph the Pet Skunk*, by John L. George and Jean George, published by E. P. Dutton & Company, Inc., Sycamore Will and Meph become fast friends. Even though the skunk eventually takes to the woods to find a mate, he returns to the boy from time to time and always remembers him. Only once does he spray his friend.

THE BORROWERS

Mary Norton

What happens to all the small objects that get lost around the house — the safety pins, matchboxes, thimbles, and the like? There are those who say that the little people "borrow" them. Oh, you don't believe in little people? Then meet Pod, resourceful head of a family that lives in a hole underneath the grandfather clock. Meet his wife, Homily, and his daughter, Arrietty. Visit their living room, papered with scraps of old letters out of the wastebasket, with stamps on the walls for pictures, and red blotting paper on the floor for a rug. Find out what happens when their presence in the house is discovered by a boy, who later makes friends with Arrietty.

So ARRIETTY told the boy about borrowing — how difficult it was and how dangerous. She told him about the storerooms under the floor; about Pod's early exploits, the skill he had shown and the courage; she described those far-off days, before her birth, when Pod and Homily had been rich; she described the musical snuffbox of gold filigree, and the little bird which flew out of it made of kingfisher feathers, how it flapped its wings and sang its song; she described the doll's wardrobe and the tiny green glasses; the little silver teapot out of the drawing-room case; the satin bedcovers and embroidered sheets . . . "those we have still," she told him, "they're Her handkerchiefs . . ." "She," the boy realized gradually, was his Great-Aunt Sophy upstairs, bedridden since a hunting accident some twenty years before; he

240

heard how Pod would borrow from Her room, picking his way — in the firelight — among the trinkets on Her dressing table, even climbing Her bed-curtains and walking on Her quilt. And of how She would watch him and sometimes talk to him because, Arrietty explained, every day at six o'clock they brought Her a decanter of Fine Old Pale Madeira, and how before midnight She would drink the lot. Nobody blamed Her, not even Homily, because, as Homily would say, She had so few pleasures, poor soul, but, Arrietty explained, after the first three glasses Great-Aunt Sophy never believed in anything she saw. "She thinks my father comes out of the decanter," said Arrietty, "and one day when I'm older he's going to take me there and She'll think I come out of the decanter too. It'll please Her, my father thinks, as She's used to him now. Once he took my mother, and She perked up like anything and kept asking after her and why didn't she come any more and saying they'd watered the Madeira because once, She says, She saw a little man *and* a little woman and now she only sees a little man . . ."

"I wish she thought I came out of the decanter," said the boy. "She gives me dictation and teaches me to write. I only see her in the mornings when she's cross. She sends for me and looks behind my ears and asks Mrs. D. if I've learned my words."

"What does Mrs. D. look like?" asked Arrietty. (How delicious it was to say "Mrs. D." like that . . . how careless and daring!)

"She's fat and has a mustache and gives me my bath and hurts my bruise and my sore elbow and says she'll take a slipper to me one of these days . . ." The boy pulled up a tuft of grass and stared at it angrily and Arrietty saw his lip tremble. "My mother's very nice," he said. "She lives in India. Why did you lose all your worldly riches?"

"Well," said Arrietty, "the kitchen boiler burst and hot water came pouring through the floor into our house and everything was washed away and piled up in front of the grating. My father worked night and day. First hot,

then cold. Trying to salvage things. And there's a dreadful draught in March through that grating. He got ill, you see, and couldn't go borrowing. So my Uncle Hendreary had to do it and one or two others and my mother gave them things, bit by bit, for all their trouble. But the kingfisher bird was spoilt by the water; all its feathers fell off and a great twirly spring came jumping out of its side. My father used the spring to keep the door shut against draughts from the grating and my mother put the feathers in a little moleskin hat. After a while I got born and my father went borrowing again. But he gets tired now and doesn't like curtains, not when any of the bobbles are off . . ."

"I helped him a bit," said the boy, "with the tea cup. He was shivering all over. I suppose he was frightened."

"My father frightened!" exclaimed Arrietty angrily. "Frightened of you!" she added.

"Perhaps he doesn't like heights," said the boy.

"He loves heights," said Arrietty. "The thing he doesn't like is curtains. I've told you. Curtains make him tired."

The boy sat thoughtfully on his haunches, chewing a blade of grass. "Borrowing," he said after a while. "Is that what you call it?"

"What else could you call it?" asked Arrietty.

"I'd call it stealing."

Arrietty laughed. She really laughed. "But we *are* Borrowers," she explained, "like you're a — a human bean or whatever it's called. We're part of the house. You might as well say that the fire grate steals the coal from the coal scuttle."

"Then what is stealing?"

Arrietty looked grave. "Don't you know?" she asked. "Stealing is — well, supposing my Uncle Hendreary borrowed an emerald watch from Her dressing-table and my father took it and hung it up on our wall. That's stealing."

"An emerald watch!" exclaimed the boy.

"Well, I just said that because we have one on the wall at home, but my father borrowed it himself. It needn't be a watch. It could be anything. A lump of sugar even. But Borrowers don't steal."

242

"Except from human beings," said the boy.

Arrietty burst out laughing; she laughed so much that she had to hide her face in the primrose. "Oh dear," she gasped with tears in her eyes, "you are funny!" She stared upward at his puzzled face. "Human beans are *for* Borrowers — like bread's for butter!"

The boy was silent awhile. A sigh of wind rustled the cherry tree and shivered among the blossoms.

"Well, I don't believe it," he said at last, watching the falling petals. "I don't believe that's what we're for at all and I don't believe we're dying out!"

"Oh, goodness!" exclaimed Arrietty impatiently, staring up at his chin. "Just use your common sense: you're the only real human bean I ever saw (although I do just know of three more — Crampfurl, Her, and Mrs. Driver). But I know lots and lots of Borrowers: the Overmantels and the Harpsichords and the Rain-Barrels and the Linen-Presses and the Boot-Racks and the Hon. John Studdingtons and —"

He looked down. "John Studdington? But he was our grand-uncle —"

"Well, this family lived behind a picture," went on Arrietty, hardly listening, "and there were the Stove-Pipes and the Bell-Pulls and the —"

"Yes," he interrupted, "but did you see them?"

"I saw the Harpsichords. And my mother was a Bell-Pull. The others were before I was born . . ."

He leaned closer. "Then where are they now? Tell me that."

"My Uncle Hendreary has a house in the country," said Arrietty coldly, edging away from his great lowering face; it was misted over, she noticed, with hairs of palest gold. "And four children, Harpsichords and Clocks."

"But where are the others?"

"Oh," said Arrietty, "they're somewhere." But where? she wondered. And she shivered slightly in the boy's cold shadow which lay about her, slantwise, on the grass.

He drew back again, his fair head blocking out a great piece of sky. "Well," he said deliberately after a moment, and his eyes were cold, "I've only seen two Borrowers but I've seen hundreds and hundreds and hundreds and hundreds and hundreds —"

"Oh no —" whispered Arrietty.

"Of human beings." And he sat back.

Arrietty stood very still. She did not look at him. After a while she said: "I don't believe you."

"All right," he said, "then I'll tell you —"

"I still won't believe you," murmured Arrietty.

"Listen!" he said. And he told her about railway stations and football matches and racecourses and royal processions and Albert Hall concerts. He told her about India and China and North America and the British Commonwealth. He told her about the July sales. "Not hundreds," he said, "but thousands and millions and billions and trillions of great, big, enormous people. Now do you believe me?"

Arrietty stared up at him with frightened eyes: it gave her a crick in the neck. "I don't know," she whispered.

"As for you," he went on, leaning

closer again, "I don't believe that there are any more Borrowers anywhere in the world. I believe you're the last three," he said.

Arrietty dropped her face into the primrose. "We're not. There's Aunt Lupy and Uncle Hendreary and all the cousins."

"I bet they're dead," said the boy. "And what's more," he went on, "no one will ever believe I've seen *you*. And you'll be the very last because you're the youngest. One day," he told her, smiling triumphantly, "you'll be the only Borrower left in the world!"

He sat still, waiting, but she did not look up. "Now you're crying," he remarked after a moment.

"They're not dead," said Arrietty in a muffled voice; she was feeling in her little pocket for a handkerchief. "They live in a badger's set two fields away, beyond the spinney. We don't see them because it's too far. There are weasels and things and cows and foxes . . . and crows . . ."

"Which spinney?" he asked.

"I don't. know!" Arrietty almost shouted. "It's along by the gas-pipe — a field called Parkin's Beck." She blew

her nose. "I'm going home," she said.

"Don't go," he said, "not yet."

"Yes, I'm going," said Arrietty.

His face turned pink. "Let me just get the book," he pleaded.

"I'm not going to read to you now," said Arrietty.

"Why not?"

She looked at him with angry eyes. "Because —"

"Listen," he said, "I'll go to that field. I'll go and find Uncle Hendreary. And the cousins. And Aunt Whatever-she-is. And, if they're alive, I'll tell you. What about that? You could write them a letter and I'd put it down the hole —"

Arrietty gazed up at him. "Would you?" she breathed.

"Yes, I would. Really I would. Now can I go and get the book? I'll go in by the side door."

"All right," said Arrietty absently. Her eyes were shining. "When can I give you the letter?"

"Any time," he said, standing above her. "Where in the house do you live?"

"Well —" began Arrietty and stopped. Why once again did she feel this chill? Could it only be his shadow . . . towering above her, blotting out the sun? "I'll put it somewhere," she said hurriedly. "I'll put it under the hall mat."

"Which one? The one by the front door?"

"Yes, that one."

He was gone. And she stood there alone in the sunshine, shoulder deep in grass. What had happened seemed too big for thought; she felt unable to believe it really had happened: not only had she been "seen" but she had been talked to; not only had she been talked to but she had —

"Arrietty!" said a voice.

She stood up startled and spun round: there was Pod, moon-faced, on the path looking up at her. "Come on down!" he whispered.

She stared at him for a moment as though she did not recognize him; how round his face was, how kind, how familiar!

"Come on!" he said again, more urgently; and obediently, because he sounded worried, she slithered quickly toward him off the bank, balancing her primrose. "Put that thing down," he said sharply, when she stood at last beside him on the path. "You can't lug great flowers about — you got to carry a bag. What you want to go up there for?" he grumbled as they moved off across the stones. "I might never have seen you. Hurry up now. Your mother'll have tea waiting!"

Conclusion:

The "borrowers" believe that humans are dying out, and most humans believe that the little people are fast disappearing, if — indeed — they ever existed at all. In *The Borrowers*, by Mary Norton, published by Harcourt, Brace and Company, Arrietty and the boy try hard to find the answer.

THE LITTLE LADY'S ROSES
Eleanor Farjeon

As a child, Eleanor Farjeon used to delight in browsing among the dusty overflow volumes from her father's library which were kept in what the family called "the little bookroom." Later, many of these stories found their way into Miss Farjeon's wonderful anthologies which are such a rich source of pleasure for today's boys and girls. The following is a selection from The Little Bookroom, *Eleanor Farjeon's Short Stories for Children, published by Henry Z. Walck, Inc.*

DOWN IN THE VALLEY was the village, where John and Mary lived with their Mother and Father in a little cottage and went to school when the bell rang in the little schoolhouse on weekdays; and to church when the bells rang in the little church on Sundays.

And up on the hill was the great mansion, where the Little Lady lived all by herself with her servants, and paced up and down the long flight of stone steps between the cypresses and orange trees, or walked in her rose garden, which was the loveliest in the world.

The hill was high and the valley was deep, so people seldom went up or came down; only a silvery river flowed between the high mansion and the low cottages, and seemed to bind them together.

When they were out of school, Mary helped her Mother in the kitchen, and

the red rose and Mary the white one, and home they ran with their prizes.

When their parents saw the roses, the Father said, "By my Shovel and Hoe! If I could grow roses like *that* in my garden I'd be a proud man!" And the Mother cried, "Dear bless my Cherry Tart! If I could have roses like *them* in the home I'd be a glad woman!"

Then the Father asked, "Where did you get 'em, children?"

"They came down the river from the top of the hill," said John.

"Ah!" sighed the Father, "then they came from the Little Lady's rose garden, and are not for the likes of us."

before she was ten could bake little pies fit for a queen. And John dug in the garden with his Father, and before he was twelve could raise cabbages fit for a king. In their free time the children played in the fields with their schoolfellows, or paddled in the shallow pools of the river as it flowed down the middle of the valley.

One hot June day as they were splashing in the shallows they saw in the distance two tiny specks floating toward them.

"Here come the boats!" cried John.

"With red and white sails," said Mary.

"I'll have the red one," said John; and Mary said,

"I'll have the white."

But as the tiny craft came nearer, the children saw they were not boats, but roses.

They had never seen such roses for color, size, and perfume. John captured

And he went out to hoe cabbages, while the Mother rolled her paste.

But John and Mary stole out of the cottage, and John said to Mary, "Let us find the Little Lady's rose garden, and beg her for a rose tree to make our parents proud and happy."

"How shall we find it?" said Mary.

"We'll take the road up the hill that the roses took down."

"What road is that?" said Mary.

"The river," said John.

So they followed the river uphill till they came near the top, and were stopped by a big iron gate that led to the longest flight of steps they'd ever seen. On the steps the Little Lady herself paced slowly up, and when she reached the fountain at the top she turned, and paced slowly down again. At the bottom of the steps she saw the little faces of John and Mary pressed against the bars.

"What are you doing?" said John.

"Counting the steps," said the Little Lady.

"Why?" said Mary.

"Because I've nothing else to do," said the Little Lady.

"Why don't you go and hoe cabbages?" said John.

"My Head Gardener won't let me."

"Why don't you go and bake pies?" said Mary.

"My Head Cook would be cross with me."

"Father lets *me* hoe cabbages!" said John.

"Mother lets *me* bake pies!" said Mary.

"How lucky you are!" said the Little Lady. "Who are you?"

"John," said John.

"Mary," said Mary.

"Where do you come from?"

"The village in the valley."

"What have you come for?"

"A red rose tree for Father," said John.

"A white one for Mother," said Mary.

"OH!" cried the Little Lady, "did *you* find the roses I sent down the river? How glad I am!"

"Why did you send them down?" asked John.

"To bring someone back. You can't think how dull it is with nobody to play with. If you'll stay and play with

me, you shall have a rose tree apiece, and my Head Gardener won't know the difference."

So John and Mary stayed all day with the Little Lady, playing in her rose garden and her grand rooms till they were tired. And she sent them home with a rose tree apiece, which they took to their parents, saying that they had had the happiest day of their lives.

But next morning the Little Lady found counting the steps duller than ever, so when she reached the gate she opened it for the very first time and ran down the hill. On reaching the village she went straight to John and Mary's cottage, walked in, and said,

"I want to bake pies and hoe cabbages."

"Bless my Apple Dumpling, so you shall!" said the Mother.

So first the Little Lady got her hands as white as flour, and then as black as earth; and when she went home she took a cabbage and a pastry with her,

and said it was the happiest day of *her* life.

After this, whenever she was lonely, she knew she had only to run down the hill herself, or set a rose sailing to bring up a child. A white rose brought a girl, but a red rose brought a boy.

And sometimes she gathered a whole skirtful of roses and set them afloat; and on those days every child in the village was seen to be running up the hill to the Little Lady's rose garden.

THE BLUE CAT OF CASTLE TOWN
Catherine Cate Coblentz

Any kitten has a hard enough time finding a hearth to fit his song. But a blue kitten has the hardest time of all, for he must find a hearth to fit the river's song. Not only that, but he must teach the owner of the hearth to sing the song. If he fails, the days of the land may be numbered. Pity the blue cat of Castle Town, whose responsibility was especially great, for Castle Town was about to fall under a dark spell. The river had warned the blue cat never to sing the song for Arunah Hyde, but to keep an eye out for a girl with an ugly name who might — just might — listen. But the blue cat forgot, and fell in the clutches of the evil Arunah. By the time he escaped he was half dead and had lost the song. And then the yellow barn cat came to the rescue.

WHEN NEXT the blue cat opened his eyes, he was curled in a comfortable nest of dried clover, Queen Anne's lace, and chicory, in the corner of a warm and comfortable haymow. He could hear cows in their stanchions stirring and munching at their hay. Some hens were clucking softly. A stream of sunlight coming through a little dust-covered window sifted down warmly upon him. A spider worked at her web.

Sweet fragrance from the hay rose all about. Everything in that place was filled with beauty and peace and content. Everything, that is, except the blue cat. His stomach was empty — horribly empty. One cannot see beauty or know peace, and certainly no one can be content with an empty stomach.

Just then, picking her way quietly over the haymow, came the yellow tabby with the friendly mew. From her mouth hung a nice fat mouse. The tabby hurried when she saw the blue cat's hungry eyes. With a flourish of her tail she laid the mouse down in front of him. Then, head on one side, she withdrew a bit to watch.

"Mmmm," purred the blue cat gratefully, when his stomach was mouseful and comfortable. "Mmmm, that was a breakfast fit for a king."

"I never heard of such," said the

tabby cat. "But being only a barn cat, there are many things of which I never heard. If I were a blue cat, like you, matters would be quite different. Are you a king?"

The blue cat's old pride came over him and for a moment he fairly swelled with importance, although he knew no more about kings than the barn cat. Still the word, when she said it, sounded important.

"I am the blue cat," he said. "And I know the song — the song — Why! What is the song I know?"

The barn cat shook her head. "I sing my own song, the song of the hunter. I am the best mouser in Castle Town. In time I expect to catch rats!"

"*Sing your own song*," said the blue cat wonderingly. "That is it! Or at least that is the beginning. But what about the rest of the song? And what am I to do with it?"

"Don't worry about that until you are stronger," urged the barn cat. And she mewed until the blue cat followed her to the bowl of milk in a stable corner.

"It is there every night," said the barn cat. "Sylvanus Guernsey filled the bowl last night. Tonight Zeruah, his daughter, will fill it. For every winter Sylvanus goes away. He walks all the way back to Connecticut where he works for other folk until spring. Then he returns to Castle Town and makes spinning wheels. Most folk do not buy them any more. But Sylvanus likes to make them. Zeruah will be lonely this winter, for her mother has died.

"Besides Zeruah does not like to do anything. But she will care for us creatures in the barn after a fashion, though she does not make friends with us. She does not make friends with anyone. She is not good-looking and she is certain nobody likes her."

Just then Zeruah herself lifted the latch of the barn door and came in, milking pail on her arm.

The blue cat shook his head in a startled fashion. "Mew! Mew!" Why, this was the girl on whose doorstone he had sat in his kittenhood, on the long-ago day when he had first started out to sing the song — the song . . . Oh, dear, he would never remember! And if he didn't, something terrible was bound to happen, because he, the blue cat, would have failed in . . . What was it he would have failed in?

Over and over, day after day, the blue cat pondered these questions. The bright leaves fell from the trees, the last asters and goldenrod disappeared, the maples and sumac lost their brave scarlet, the bronze of the fern fronds dulled. The birds flew south.

The wind howled and moaned. Then the snow came, flake after flake, thicker and thicker, swirling in gusts, beating at the frost-covered window high in the barn, sifting in the door when Zeruah came with the milkpails.

It was cold. But the creatures were not cold. The cows chewed their cuds contentedly, there was the warm clucking of hens, the friendly baa, baa of a sheep. Prowling over the hay, in his thick fur coat, or curled in the comfortable nest, well supplied with mice by the barn cat, and bowls of milk by Zeruah, sometimes the blue cat forgot the song he had lost, forgot too that he had a mission to perform.

He would listen to the barn cat mewing her concern about Zeruah, until he, too, felt anxious about the lonely girl. This was strange, for until that winter, he had thought only about himself.

Of course he had reason to be grateful to Zeruah, he reminded himself. And even more grateful to the yellow barn cat.

"How can I ever repay you?" he asked the barn cat more than once. "I cannot catch even one mouse."

Mousing was something his mother had not taught him. It wasn't her fault, he explained. It was simply that as a kitten he had other matters to attend to.

"I see," the barn cat said politely. "What matters?"

"The matter of learning the song . . . Well, the song I have lost," explained the blue cat. And his voice held such a wailing note that the barn cat thought he must be hungry and stole off to catch another mouse.

Little by little that winter some memories came back to the blue cat. He did remember that he was looking for someone in Castle Town who would understand his song, and to whom he should teach that song. Then he would be given a hearth to sleep on. And then — something else would happen. Something important for Castle Town itself. Something in which Arunah Hyde was concerned.

And having remembered Arunah, the cat remembered Ebenezer Southmayd and John Gilroy. Little by little he put everything he recalled together. Until at last he had the story of his life, everything that is, except the song which he had once sung so proudly. The song — the song . . .

At last the cat sighed a long sigh. He could, he was positive, remember

a little lonely. And here the ray of sun sought him out.

The sun did have a feel of spring about it. And when spring came how could a blue cat stay placidly in a barn? Besides, he would soon be too great a burden for the barn cat. How could she expect to catch mice for four? His own mother, he recalled, had thought it difficult to catch mice for two.

Once the blue cat made up his mind, there was — as his mother could have told you — no changing it. So he went immediately to tell the barn cat of his decision. "It is not spring yet, but it will be soon," he said. "And I think I

no more. He must have lost the song somewhere in Castle Town, lost it as he fled desperately from Arunah.

A ray of sunlight sifted through the little window above him. Warm sunlight with the feel of spring about it. In another corner of the mow two yellow kittens called to their mother. The blue cat stalked over to look at them. They were round yellow balls with perky ears and pointed tails, and they looked much like the barn cat.

"Nice enough, as kittens go," decided the blue cat, not realizing he had spoken aloud.

"Nice enough?" echoed the barn cat, leaping unexpectedly from the rafters, and pushing the blue cat aside. "Why these are the most wonderful kittens in all Vermont!"

"Hmm!" answered the blue cat, moving away. And this time, strictly under his breath, he said, "What poor judgment you have, barn cat."

He went off by himself to the farthest mow, and lay down blinking, and

had better get an early start. I have, as you know, a great many matters to attend to." He thanked her then for all she had done. "Sometime," he insisted, "I will repay you. And the girl Zeruah, as well."

"But where," asked the barn cat, "are you going? And what will you do?"

"I am going back the way I came," he told her. "To search for the song. It must be lying under the snow somewhere in Castle Town. And if I search hard enough I shall find it. I feel *that* in my bones."

"Well, after all, you are not a blue cat for nothing," answered the barn cat.

Conclusion:

The blue cat has many amazing adventures before he finally fulfills his mission. They make fascinating reading in *The Blue Cat of Castle Town*, by Catherine Cate Coblentz, published by Longmans, Green & Company.

DUSTING IS FUN

Sydney Taylor

They were called the "all-of-a-kind family" because the five little sisters ranging in age from four to twelve, usually dressed alike. What a wonderful mother and father they had, and what good times! They may have lived on New York City's lower East Side, but they wouldn't have changed places with five royal princesses. Even the daily chores could be made fun when mother put her mind to it.

AFTER BREAKFAST Monday morning, Mama said, "Henny, put aside your book. It's your turn to dust the front room today."

"Mama, let Ella do it," Henny said. "I have to finish my homework."

"I will not," retorted Ella, her black eyes snapping. "It's your turn. I did it yesterday."

"Ella is right," Mama said. "You should have done your homework yesterday instead of leaving it until the last moment. You'll have to do it."

"Then let Charlotte do it. She hasn't done a thing all morning. I've got to finish my homework."

"Charlotte will help dry the breakfast dishes this morning. That's her job today. Your job today is to dust the front room."

"All right, then. I'll have a swell excuse when the teacher asks me why I haven't finished my homework. I'll say my mother took up all my time with dusting." Henny tossed her blonde curls defiantly. How her sisters envied her those curls!

She slammed the front-room door as she went in to perform her job. Mama knew it would be a job badly done. She sighed. She was tired of the girls forever trying to avoid doing this chore. She would have to think of something.

After the children had gone to school, Mama thought. Frequently she smiled. She got out her sewing box and began rummaging in it, picking out a dozen colored buttons. Then she put the box away and went back to her work, humming softly to herself.

The following morning Mama put the buttons in her apron pocket and went into the front room, closing the door. The children stared after her and then looked at one another.

"Say, do you think Mama is going to dust the front room herself this morning?" Henny asked.

"She didn't have a dust rag with her," Ella said.

"Maybe she's looking around to see how dusty the room is," came from Charlotte.

Mama was in the front room for a few minutes. When she came out, she was smiling.

"Well, girls," she said, "we're going to play a game and I've been getting the room ready for it."

The children became very interested. "What game?"

"It's a game of hide-and-seek," Mama answered. "I have hidden a dozen buttons in the front room. If the one who dusts can find those twelve buttons, she will have done a wonder-

ful dusting job, and I won't even have to check up on her. Now let's see, whose turn is it to dust today."

"It's my turn, my turn!" shouted Sarah.

"Aw, Ma! Let me do it today!"

"No, me!"

The children fought for a chance at the hated chore. Even baby Gertie who had never been expected to do so before, now was eager to try her hand at it.

"It's really Sarah's turn," Mama said. "So in you go, Sarah. I expect you to bring back twelve buttons."

Sarah took up the dustcloth and fairly skipped out of the kitchen. In a minute she was back again. "Forgot the stool," she explained. Eight-year-old Sarah was still too small to reach the high places without the aid of a stool. Now fully armed with dustcloth and stool, she disappeared into the front room, while her sisters watched enviously.

"You needn't be so unhappy," Mama told them. "You'll each get your turn at the game when your dusting day comes."

Sarah stood still beside the closed

door of the front room and looked about her. Such a big room, she thought. So many good hiding places in all its furnishings. What would be the best way to hunt?

I guess I'd better dust the same way I always do, she finally decided, and proceeded towards the big table standing in the middle of the room. She removed the fruit bowl that was set in the exact center of the table. She dusted the big family album that rested at one end. No time today to examine the pictures of a youthful Papa and Mama without any children. Today she had to hunt for buttons, so she

put the album on a chair without even opening it. Then she removed the tablecloth. No button here. She got down on the thick red-and-green carpet to dust the table leg. At the base of the leg staring up at her lay a shiny red button. Sarah's eyes began to dance with excitement. This was going to be fun! Button number one was slipped into her apron pocket.

The table was finished and cover and objects replaced. Chairs were carefully dusted next. They were hard to do, and Mama had five of them. The first yielded nothing. Neither did the sec-

ond. The third had a button slid in neatly in one of the hard-to-dust places in its back. Button number two hit button number one with a click as it was deposited in Sarah's apron pocket.

The last two chairs were dusted but no more buttons turned up. Sarah stood on the stool to dust off the top of the upright piano. She dusted off each knickknack thoroughly, and hopefully lifted the piano cover so that she might wipe the wood smooth of dirt. Her effort was rewarded, for there lying peacefully on the piano top was button number three.

Now Sarah was tempted to give up cleaning the rest of the piano. There was so much to it and surely Mama wouldn't put two buttons in one piece of furniture. Still it wouldn't be playing the game fair and, besides, one never could tell. Mama might be trying to catch her in just such a trick. Sarah dusted the foot pedals, but found no buttons. Nor were there any on the lid covering the keyboard. Piano keys had to be kept clean, too, so up went the lid. And there was another button!

Sarah was jubilant. She carried the stool over to the mantel shelf. Up she went, dustcloth tight in one hand. Now she could lift the china shepherd and shepherdess. She liked to handle these, especially the shepherdess, so dainty in her pink-and-blue dress with tiny rosebuds on it. She picked her up first. Something rattled! In the opening at the back of the little lady, which was for flowers, Mama had put button number five. And that was all Sarah found on the mantel shelf.

Two small round tables stood in front of the lace-curtained windows. Sarah started to work on these. On the first she discovered nothing, but under the doily which decorated the top of the second table, she found the sixth button.

Mama wanted her helpers to dust window sills. Sarah remembered and, because she did, she was able to add both the seventh and eighth buttons to her apron pocket. Sitting right on the floor near the white window woodwork was button number nine. If Sarah had neglected the woodwork, she never would have found it.

She stopped in front of the tall mirror that stood between the windows, and began making faces at herself. "Now where shall I hunt for three more buttons?" she asked her reflection.

As she looked about, Sarah's eyes fell on the colored calendar that Mama had hung on the wall. This is a new month, she thought. I might as well change the calendar while I'm here. Neatly Sarah tore off the sheet that said November, 1912.

She got down on the rug and looked about the room thoughtfully. Pretty nearly everything had been gone over, excepting the large sea shells lying on the floor on each side of the mirror. Sarah liked these shells. If she held one close to her ear, she could hear a strange noise like the roaring of waves. She picked up a shell, dusted it off, and held it close to her ear for a minute, listening. She hoped a button would pop out but there was no button, only the same rushing sound. Sarah picked up the second shell and a button looked up at her. Ten buttons found — only two more to go.

All that was left was the woodwork. Sarah dusted the door first, for the ridge near the bottom was such a dust-gathering place. And right there on the flooring below the door ridge was button number eleven!

The baseboards about the entire room were dusted, but there was still one button missing. That meant Sarah had overlooked something, but what? Had she dusted the underneath part of the second table or had she forgotten to do it in the excitement of finding the button under the doily? Well, she'd do it again just to make sure. She was very glad indeed that she did make sure for there on the table's curved-up leg reposed button number twelve!

She threw open the front-room door and came running into the kitchen, crying out joyfully: "I found them! I

found them all, every single one of them! Ma, you certainly picked some swell hiding places! But it was fun. I'd like to do it again!"

For the next week Mama had a beautifully clean front room and there was not a single grumble.

After that the children might have tired of the game and Mama would have been right back where she started. But she was a wise mother. At the end of the week, the buttons went back into the sewing box. Mama said she didn't have time to put the buttons out every morning. From now on, they would be hidden only occasionally. No child would know just when she might find buttons during her dusting because Mama would hide the buttons at night after the girls had gone to sleep. Also the number would be different, sometimes six, sometimes ten.

Mama was as good as her word. Sometimes she brought out her buttons once or twice during the week. Sometimes she would let two weeks pass by without producing them. And then every day in one memorable week, Mama hid buttons *plus* one shiny copper penny. "Finders-keepers," she told the little dusters.

The grumbling didn't stop completely, but it was not nearly so loud or so often. And in the meantime, the children were taught to be the best little housekeepers in the whole world.

Conclusion:

Would you like to share more adventures in the lives of these five little girls? Read about their trip to Coney Island and about their happy Jewish holidays in *All-of-a-kind Family,* by Sydney Taylor, published by Follett Publishing Company.

SATURDAY FIVE

Elizabeth Enright

The four Melendy children — Mona, Rush, Randy, and Oliver — lived in an old brownstone house in New York City with their father and Cuffy, the housekeeper. Like children everywhere, they considered Saturday a very important day in the week — so important that they formed the Independent Saturday Afternoon Adventure Club and pooled their allowances each week so that one member could have a really good spree. This story tells what six-year-old Oliver did with all that money when his Saturday rolled around.

AFTER AWHILE, very slowly, it began to be spring. There were rust-colored buds on the ailanthus trees, and one day Mona heard a blue jay in the back yard sounding countryfied and out of place. Pretty soon it would be time to go to the valley; back to the rambling old wooden house that the Melendys rented every summer. Mona was homesick thinking about it, and got all her summer clothes out of their boxes to see if she had outgrown them (which she had, and Randy was glad because now they would descend to her) and forgot to put them away again until Cuffy got after her. Rush took his baseball bat to school, and Randy wrote a poem. Oliver spent hours in the back yard digging fortifications in the mud. The seats and knees of his overalls were a constant source of despair for Cuffy.

The Independent Saturday Afternoon Adventure Club had so far been entirely successful. Randy had spent her second Saturday at the Ballet Theatre and was now able to walk on her toes quite easily, and had made a ballet skirt out of five pairs of muslin curtains that couldn't be darned any more. Rush had gone to hear Rudolf Serkin play the piano, and had been practicing furiously ever since in the hours that were not occupied by school or baseball. Mona had seen Katharine Cornell in a play and was very hard to live with as a result. She now moved queenlike and distant through a world of her own.

But this particular Saturday was Oliver's, and they had agreed to stay home. Not that he could go out by himself, of course, as they could; but in order to make him feel like a proper member of the I.S.A.A.C., they respected his Saturday and stayed at home. Also, besides giving him back the three dimes he had lent them, each added a dime of his own. "That'll be almost half what we have to spend on our Saturdays, and it will look like a million dollars to him," Rush said; it was his idea.

The day passed pleasantly enough. There was lemon pie for dessert at lunch, and afterwards Rush and Randy gave Isaac a bath in the basement washtub. He was philosophical about this ordeal by now and stood passive, though loathing every minute of it. When he was dry, they took him for a walk to show him off. Mona didn't want to go because she had borrowed some of Cuffy's big steel hairpins and was doing her hair in a pompadour just for an experiment.

The walk was a great success, and so was Isaac. People stopped them frequently to admire and pat him; and every time they asked what kind of dog he was, Rush gave them a different answer in a polite, serious voice. A Bronx beagle, he might say, or a Central Park setter, or an Interborough Rapid Transit retriever. Randy almost died.

When they came back to their own block, they could see Mona hanging out of the second-story window of their house.

"Where's Oliver?" she called, when they drew near.

Rush and Randy looked at her blankly.

"I don't know. Where is he?" shouted Rush.

"Isn't he home?" cried Randy.

"We can't find him *any* place," answered Mona, withdrawing her head and closing the window with a bang.

They ran up the steps and into the house. Cuffy looked pale and distracted. "Rush, you go down the street to the Potters' and see if by any chance he's gone to play with Petey, though goodness knows he's *never* done such a thing before. Randy, you run round the block. Maybe he's trying out his roller skates again."

"Maybe he's just hiding," suggested Randy.

"His coat and cap are gone," Mona told her. "And anyway I've looked *every*where. In all the closets and underneath the beds. Even in the trunks in the basement."

"Where's Father?"

"Gone to Philadelphia to lecture. He won't be back till five and we don't know where to get him. Hurry up, Randy, run along."

At that moment the object of all this concern was seated comfortably at Madison Square Garden. His knees were crossed, he was leaning back with a bottle of pop in one hand, and watching a lady in spangles hanging by her teeth to a rope fifty feet above the ground.

It had all been very simple, but it was also a well-thought-out campaign. Four weeks ago Oliver had received seven dimes which he had prudently concealed in one of his last summer's sandals. Today he had received seven more, which together with the sandal money made fourteen dimes. Untold wealth, but he did not let it go to his head. Everything proceeded according to plan.

Today when he was supposed to be resting he had got up, put on his coat and cap, and walked, faintly jingling, right out of the house. There was no trouble of any kind. When he got to Fifth Avenue he went up to a police-man and said, "Where is the circus, please?"

And the policeman said, "Madison Square Garden. Aren't you kinda young to be out alone?"

Oliver simply said, "No, I don't think so," and went his way. When he came to another policeman some blocks farther on he went up to him and said, "Where is Madison Square Garden, please?"

"Going to the circus, eh?" said the policeman. "It's at Fiftieth Street and Eighth Avenue. You all alone?"

Oliver simply said, "Yes, I am," and proceeded on his way, leaving the po-liceman with his hands full of traffic.

At Fiftieth Street he went up to another policeman and said, "Which way is Eighth Avenue, please?"

"That way," said the policeman, jerking a white cotton thumb westward. "'Bout three blocks over. Ain't nobody with you?"

Oliver simply said, "No, nobody," and crossed the street with the red light.

It was easy when he got there too. He just stood in a long line of grownups and children and held tight to his dimes and listened to what the people in front of him said when they got to the window. So when he got there he was able to say, "One, please. The kind that costs one dollar," and count out ten dimes slowly and carefully. The man behind the window had to peer down in order to see him at all. Then holding his ticket tightly he followed close behind a large family and tried hard to look like one of them.

"Like to hold your own ticket, eh, sonny?" said the ticket man.

"Yes, I do," replied Oliver, and entered the magic portals. It was wonderful. It smelled of elephants the minute you got in, even before you came to the real circus part. Breathing the smell deeply, Oliver climbed some steps that a uniformed man told him to, and then walked along a corridor that another uniformed man told him to. He thought he heard a lion roar some place, and his feet crunched on peanut shells. It was very exciting. Finally he came to the right door, entered it, and found himself in another world. It was a vast world, carpeted with blue sawdust and walled with thousands of faces. A complicated web of cables and rope ladders and nets rose from the huge arena to misty regions high overhead. On the blue sawdust at the bottom there were three large caged rings, and in each of these rings the most extraordinary things were happening.

"This way, Bud," said the usher, steering the bedazzled Oliver to a seat. Oliver sat down without knowing that he did so. After a long time he removed his coat and cap blindly, never taking his eyes off the ring nearest him. In it three lions, two bears, and a black leopard were climbing ladders, while on high gold stools seven other lions sat and snarled and batted with their paws at their trainer who was the bravest man in the world and wore a red coat. He could make those animals do anything. Before he was through, one of the bears was pushing the other in a huge baby carriage while all the lions, on a bridge overhead, sat up on their hind legs and begged. Oliver sighed deeply: it was almost too much. His only regret was that he was too busy watching his ring to pay attention to the others. The air rang with the crack of whips and the sharp commands of the trainers.

As the cages were dismantled and the animals taken away, Oliver began to notice the men who were going up and down the aisles selling things: jeweled canes, and clown hats, and things to eat. They called their wares hoarsely like a lot of crows. "Hot dogs, hot dogs!" cried one, and "Getcha roasted peanuts here," cried another, and "*Ice-cole pop*," still another. But the one Oliver was most interested in was the man who kept saying "Cotton candy, Cotton c-a-a-a-n-dy," as he went by with what looked like a lot of pink birds' nests on sticks. Oliver finally bought one. It was interesting; you bit into a cloud of pink spun sugar and it instantly became nothing in your mouth. He ate it lingeringly, to make it last. All the time fascinating things were going on in the huge arena before him. Clowns came out and did their stunts, a man jumped over three elephants, ladies in spangles rode standing up on the backs of broad white horses, and dozens of tiny taffy-colored ponies, with plumes on their foreheads like the frills on lamb chops, pranced delicately about the rings and performed the most astonishing tricks. Oliver bit into his pink cloud and stared dreamily.

"I want some of that candy," said a sharp little voice at his side. Oliver turned a startled glance on the occupant of the next seat. He had forgotten there was anyone else in the world besides himself and the circus people.

"Don't bother the little boy, Marleen," said the little girl's mother in the kind of weak, uncertain way that no self-respecting child pays any attention to.

"I *want* some," repeated Marleen through her nose. She meant business. She was a very little girl and she had a pointed chin, dark eyes, black curls as stiff as cigars, a blue hair ribbon, a gold ring, and pink stuff on her tiny fingernails. Oliver detested her. He looked coldly away and went on eating his candy.

"Now, Marleen," said her mother.

"I want some. I *want* some of that boy's candy!"

"I'll get you some when the man comes by. Now you be a good girl and look at the pretty horsies."

"I want some of his. You give me that candy, boy!"

261

nificent beyond description; from zebra-drawn coaches to elephants wearing tasseled capes and jeweled howdahs. Oliver watched it raptly while eating a hot dog with mustard. He surveyed the acrobats (whose muscles seemed to stretch like garters) while eating another hot dog, this time with sauerkraut. It was forbidden Paradise. Cuffy didn't believe in hot dogs or mustard or sauerkraut, but Oliver believed in them all. By the time the aerial artists had come along he was quenching a violent thirst with a bottle of pop. (It was at this moment that his entire family was in an uproar about his disappearance.) The act was so exciting that he couldn't finish the pop till it was over, because it made his stomach feel so queer when one of the glittering creatures high overhead leaped from her fragile swing and arched through the air like a bird to the next glittering creature. The climax came when one of the creatures stood on her head on a trapeze without holding on and swung to and fro, shimmering like a dragonfly, far above the arena. It was breath-taking. Oliver felt so weak after watching her that he quickly finished his pop and purchased a bag of peanuts to fortify himself.

What a circus it was! One continual blaze of glory from beginning to end; from the flashing, bounding acrobats to the trained seals clapping their flippers; from the daring tightrope walkers to the fat clown who kept finding live ducklings in his pockets. Oliver did not want to believe it was over and sat for quite a while with people climbing over him and pushing past him, in

Oliver swallowed the last of it at a gulp and Marleen uttered a piercing scream of frustration. Heads in the row turned and looked at them. "Now, Marleen, now Marleen," said her mother helplessly. But Marleen continued to scream like a steam whistle until her mother had consoled her by buying her a cotton-candy stick of her own, and a fancy cane besides. Even then she stared unblinkingly at Oliver. She could not be persuaded to look at the arena, and after a while the consciousness of that baleful scrutiny spoiled even Oliver's enjoyment. He couldn't pay the proper attention to the jugglers. A few rows away, on the aisle, he noticed a vacant seat and after some deliberation made his way to it without a backward glance at Marleen.

After this unpleasant episode the performance progressed blissfully without a flaw. The procession was mag-

the hope that they were all mistaken and something new was about to begin in the arena.

"Whatcha waitin' for, Bud?" said the usher, coming up to him. "Don'tcha know you'll get swept up with the trash and fed to the elephants if you wait *too* long?"

Probably he doesn't mean it, Oliver thought, but he got up hastily. At first he couldn't find his coat or cap, but then he remembered he had left them in the seat from which Marleen had driven him. There they still were luckily, though littered with peanut shells and a piece of chewed chewing gum, doubtless the work of the vindictive Marleen. Oliver cleaned them off as well as he could, put them on, and after quite a lot of blundering about in the wrong direction (owing to the fact that he didn't understand the meaning of the word "exit") he found himself out on the street. Already it was dusk, and he began to hurry. For the first time the probable consequences of his adventure began to trouble him. It made him especially uncomfortable to think of Cuffy, for some reason.

And now the streets kept turning out the wrong way, and he found himself on Tenth Avenue instead of Fifth. The place looked strange; full of high, dark buildings, and big noisy boys who went bowling by him on roller skates, and shouted at him hoarsely to get out of the way. As if that weren't enough, he began to have a terrible stomachache. Though he was a calm and resourceful person, Oliver was only six years old after all. So the next move seemed to be to cry. He stumbled and

banged along the street, sobbing quietly and wiping his nose on his sleeve, wishing with all his heart that he was at home with Cuffy, and that he had never heard of hot dogs or cotton candy. Dimly he was aware of a clopping of hoofs on pavement but he was too miserable to look up until he heard a voice say:

"Whatsa matter, sonny?"

Oliver saw a big square policeman seated on a big square horse, magnificent as anything at the circus. All his buttons and two gold teeth glittered richly in the light of the street lamp.

263

"What's eatin' you?" repeated the policeman kindly.

"I'm lost!" wept Oliver. "And I'm sick at my stomach, and I want to go *home!*"

"What's your name?"

"Oliver M-Melendy."

"Know where you live?"

Oliver told him.

"Okay. You quit crying now," said the policeman. "You and me will take a little ride to your house. Think ya can hold out?"

"I guess so," replied Oliver dubiously. His stomach felt awfully unreliable. The policeman got off his horse and hoisted Oliver up on it as if he had been a kitten. Then he got on himself, behind Oliver, clucked at the horse and away they went. Oliver thought gloomily that it was probably the only time in his whole life that he was ever going to ride with a mounted policeman and he felt so sick he couldn't appreciate it.

"I guess I'm going to get a scolding when I go home," Oliver told the policeman. "Maybe I'll get a spanking too." All the shine was gone off the day.

"Why, what did you do?"

"Will you promise not to arrest me?" said Oliver cautiously.

"I doubt if it will be necessary," said the policeman, so Oliver told him.

"Well, I'll let your family take care of the penalty," the policeman decided. "It's a very serious offense all right, but it seems to me you've been punished almost enough as it is."

The traffic cop at Fifth Avenue looked at the mounted policeman and Oliver and said, "You've run in another big-time gang leader, I see."

"You'd be surprised," replied Oliver's policeman, and gave Oliver a pat on the shoulder.

At the Melendy house all was confusion. Randy was in tears. Father (who had returned from Philadelphia) and Rush were still out searching, and Cuffy was saying into the telephone, "Six years old. He has blue eyes, blond hair, and he weighs —" when the doorbell rang, and she dropped the receiver.

"Oh, Oliver darling, where *were* you?" cried Mona's voice, and Cuffy arrived to see her on her knees beside Oliver, who looked smaller and paler than ever before. Behind him stood the largest, most solid policeman she had ever seen in her life.

Aching with relief, Cuffy hugged Oliver, then she looked up at the policeman and said, "That's the quickest response I ever got from anything. I hadn't no more than just finished describing him to the police this minute —"

"The police force is never at a loss, ma'am," replied the officer with a wink.

Cuffy held Oliver away from her:

"Where in the world have you been?"

"To the circus," replied Oliver wanly.

"To the circus! Alone?" Cuffy was horrified.

"I wouldn't be too hard on him, ma'am," advised the officer.

"Go ahead and spank me if you want to," Oliver said, and was sick on the doormat.

Long, long afterwards, when all the thunder and lightning in his stomach had subsided, and the danger of a spanking was past, Oliver lay in his small bed with his hand in Father's.

"Why did you go without telling us, though?" asked Father. "You could have gone to the circus. Rush or Cuffy would have been glad to take you. I would have taken you myself if I could have stolen the time."

Oliver sighed. "I did ask Cuffy about it once, but she said oh no there's too much measles around. And everybody else was going out alone on their Saturdays, so I just thought I'd go alone too. I did want to see the circus so badly."

"Didn't you know we'd worry?"

"I guess I didn't think about it till afterwards," Oliver admitted.

"Well, you'll never give us a scare like that again, will you?"

"No, I never will, if I can help it," promised Oliver.

"All right then. That's that. Now suppose you tell me what you liked best at the circus."

"Oh, everything was wonderful. I liked the man on the one-wheel bicycle, and the elephants, and that automobile with all the clowns and the donkey in it, and the lady who stood on her head on the swing, and I liked all the things I was eating, while I was eating them. But the thing I liked *best* of all wasn't in the circus."

"What was that?" said Father.

"It was when the policeman brought me home on the horse," replied Oliver.

For now, no longer overshadowed by stomach-aches or unhappy apprehensions, the memory of that ride had become a radiant thing. He remembered the horse's two pointed ears that could move independently of each other, and its brawny, arching neck with the tidy black mane; and its strong, healthy smell. It was sort of

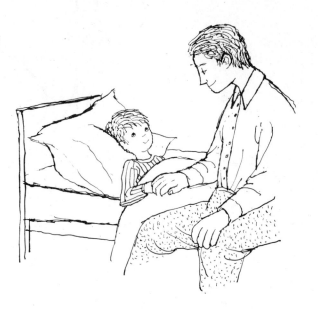

like riding on a boat, only better because it felt alive, and you were higher up. And behind, immense and gorgeous in his uniform, rode the officer of the law who had befriended him. Oliver remembered how he held the reins in white gloved hands the size of baseball mitts. The splendor of that ride would never die.

Conclusion:

In *The Saturdays,* by Elizabeth Enright, published by Rinehart & Company, you can read more about what Rush, Mona, and Randy did on each of *their* Saturdays.

AUTHOR INDEX

TITLE INDEX

SUBJECT INDEX

BOOKS RECOMMENDED IN THE NOTES

*(Titles of books from which excerpts are
included in this volume are given in italics)*

All-of-a-kind Family (Taylor)
Angus and the Cat (Flack)
Angus and the Ducks (Flack)
Angus Lost (Flack)
Around and About (Chute)
Azor (Crowley)
"B" Is for Betsy (Haywood)
Betsy-Tacy (Lovelace)
Blind Colt, The (Rounds)
Blue Cat of Castle Town, The (Coblentz)
Borrowers, The (Norton)
Charlotte's Web (White)
Chimney Corner Stories (Hutchinson)
Country Poems (Coatsworth)
Everything and Anything (Aldis)
Fairy Flute, The (Fyleman)
Far and Few (McCord)
Fast Sooner Hound, The
    (Bontemps and Conroy)
Favorite Place, The (Eberle)
Fireside Stories (Hutchinson)
First Book of Fairy Tales, The (Abell)
Five Chinese Brothers, The (Bishop)
Fog Magic (Sauer)
Folk Tales from the Philippines (Sechrist)
Giant Book of Family Fun and Games, The
    (Tedford)
Golden Egg Book, The (Brown)
Goodnight Moon (Brown)
Horn that Stopped the Band, The (Parsons)
I Go A-Traveling (Tippett)
In and Out (Robinson)
Jataka Tales (Babbitt)
Jokes, Jokes, Jokes (Hoke)
Lavender's Blue (Lines)
Li Lun, Lad of Courage (Treffinger)

Lion Boy (Stevens)
Little Bookroom, The (Farjeon)
Little Girl with Seven Names (Hunt)
Little Hill, The (Behn)
Little House in the Big Woods (Wilder)
Little Wooden Doll, The (Bianco)
Manuela's Birthday in Old Mexico (Bannon)
Meph, the Pet Skunk (George)
Merry Men of Gotham, The (Jagendorf)
Middle Sister, The (Mason)
Moffats, The (Estes)
More Jataka Tales (Babbitt)
My Father's Dragon (Gannett)
Once the Hodja (Kelsey)
Pancakes Paris (Bishop)
Pool in the Meadow (Frost)
Poppy Seed Cakes, The (Clark)
Pussycat's Christmas, A (Brown)
Red Mittens (Bannon)
Riddles, Riddles, Riddles (Leeming)
Runaway Bunny, The (Brown)
Saturdays, The (Enright)
Scary Thing, The (Bannon)
Silverhorn (Conkling)
Sneakers (Brown)
Surprise for a Cowboy (Bulla)
Tales of a Korean Grandmother (Carpenter)
Tales of Faraway Folk
    (Deutsch and Yarmolinsky)
Taxis and Toadstools (Field)
Ted and Nina Have a Happy Rainy Day
    (de Angeli)
13 Danish Tales (Hatch)
This Boy Cody (Wilson)
Twenty and Ten (Bishop)
Two and Two Are Four (Haywood)